Hebrews, James
Peter, John, Jude
Study Guide

Search-and-Discover Bible Study Series

by John E. Baird

A Division of Standard Publishing
Cincinnati, Ohio
40018

ISBN: 0-87239-026-8

Printed in U.S.A.

PREFACE

HEBREWS, JAMES, PETER, JOHN, JUDE Study Guide, one of ten workbooks in the Search-and-Discover Bible Study Series by Dr. John E. Baird, is devised to provide a comprehensive study of the New Testament. Through the use of both content and discussion questions in each study guide, the student has the opportunity to examine both the Bible statements and his own thoughts in order to accomplish his goal—a better understanding and a practical application of the New Testament teachings.

For the most effective use of this study guide, students are encouraged to complete the content questions at home. Read the Scripture verses for each lesson, answer the content questions, and then reread the verses in order to check the answers. This procedure reinforces learning of the material.

After completing the content questions, a student should read and contemplate the discussion questions in order to be prepared for class. Effective group discussion centering around the discussion questions presented in each chapter provides an opportunity for the expression of one's own thoughts, for the answering of questions, for an interesting exchange of ideas, and for suggestions about the application of the Scriptures in daily life.

The leader should prepare for the lesson in much the same way as the student. But also the leader must be prepared to answer questions, to offer new insights into the lesson, and to guide the students through their discussion in order to provide a significant learning experience for each individual. Leaders may find the following kinds of references helpful in preparing for the discussion: various translations of the Bible, a Bible commentary, a dictionary, a topical Bible, a concordance, an atlas, and wall maps.

Young people and adults both will find this series applicable for use in Sunday-school classes, evening study programs, vacation Bible school, camps, neighborhood Bible study groups, new member programs, and even family devotions.

—The Editor

CONTENTS

LESSON 1

Hebrews 1:1-14

CONTENT QUESTIONS

1. In ancient times how did God speak to people (v. 1)? ______

______

2. How did He speak in more recent times (v. 2)? ______

______

3. What did the Son have to do with creation (v. 2)? ______

______

4. How similar was the Son to God himself (v. 3)? ______

______

5. What did the Son do, after acting to remove sin (v. 3)? ______

______

6. How does the Son compare to angels (v. 4)? ______

______

7. What did God say to the Son that He never said to angels (v. 5)? ______

______

8. What did God say about the Son that He never said about an angel (v. 5)? ______

______

9. How were angels commanded to regard the Son (v. 6)? ______

______

10. What did God say, then, about angels (v. 7)? ______________

____

11. How permanent is the throne of the Son (v. 8)? ______________

____

12. What is to be the sceptre of His kingdom (v. 8)? ______________

____

13. The Son loves righteousness. What does He hate (v. 9)? ____

____

14. How was the Son anointed (v. 9)? ______________

____

15. Who laid the foundation of the earth (v. 10)? ______________

16. Who made the heavens (v. 10)? ______________

17. What does the future hold for heavens and earth (vv. 11, 12)?

____

18. In the face of the destruction of all things what happens to the Lord (v. 11)? ______________

19. How stable will the Lord be (v. 12)? ______________

____

20. What did God say to the Son that He never said to angels (v. 13)? ______________

21. What do angels do (v. 14)? ______________

____

DISCUSSION QUESTIONS

1. In what sense did God speak by the prophets? Did God actually supply the words for these men to use? If so, why don't they sound alike instead of having their individual style of writing? If God just revealed ideas to them, wouldn't they have been in danger of error in putting thoughts into words? If God spoke by the prophets, what need was there for Him to send His Son?

What do we, today, learn from the Son that we couldn't learn from the prophets?

2. Why did the writer speak of the Son as coming in the "last days" (v. 2)? How could those be the "last days" when we know the world would go on for at least 2000 years? In what sense is it possible to speak of the first century as the "last days", or was the writer mistaken? Is it proper for us to think of our own time as the "last days"? To what extent should Christians today emphasize teaching about the end of the world? Isn't there a danger that such teaching will bring criticism upon Christianity in general (see 2 Peter 3:3, 4)?

3. How do you feel about the human terms which the writer applies to God in this chapter: "Throne" (v. 8), "scepter" (v. 8), "anointed" (v. 9), "right hand" (v. 13)? Do you think these terms were helpful to ancient man in understanding God? Are they helpful to modern man? Is it possible for us to think about God without using figures such as these? If you were trying to find a modern way of picturing these things about the Father and the Son, what would you say?

4. What is the relationship between the Father and the Son? If the Son is begotten of the Father (v. 5), is the Son subordinate to the Father? How do you explain such sayings as Matthew 24:36 which seem to indicate that the Father has knowledge not given to the Son? At the same time, the writer of this chapter clearly intends to show the superiority of the Son. To whom or to what is the Son superior?

5. What is this writer teaching about the nature of God? In what sense is God a "Father"? Would it be proper to apply the term "Mother" to God? In what sense does God love righteousness and hate lawlessness (v. 9)? Isn't God by nature a God of love? In what sense is God unchanging (v. 12) and without an end to His years? What problems do you see in human beings trying to understand these aspects of God? How much do you think we could discover about God from the world of nature, without the help of special revelation? Do you think that these problems had anything to do with God speaking through His Son (v. 2)?

6. What teaching does this chapter contain about angels? Who are they? What is their function? What is their relation to God? How highly should human beings regard angels (see Galatians 1:8)?

LESSON 2

Hebrews 2:1-18

CONTENT QUESTIONS

1. Why should we give heed to what we have heard (v. 1)? ____

   ____

2. What has happened to every transgression and disobedience (v. 2)? ______________________________

3. Who first spoke of our great salvation (v. 3)? ____________

4. Who confirmed it (v. 3)? ______________________________

5. How did God bear witness (v. 4)? ______________________________

   ____

6. What can be said about the world of which the author wrote (v. 5)? ______________________________

7. What question did someone raise about man (v. 6)?

   ____

   ____

8. What status does man hold (v. 7)? ____________________

   ____

9. What authority was he given (v. 7)? ____________________

   ____

10. What things are subject to the son of man's control (v. 8)?

    ____

11. Was this control actually effective (v. 8)? ______________

12. For whose sake did Jesus taste of death (v. 9)? ___________

13. How was the Author of salvation made perfect (v. 10)? ______

____

14. How close are the sanctified to the One who sanctified them (v. 11)? ____

15. What term can be used to describe this close relationship (v. 11)? ____

16. Where will praises to God be sung (v. 12)? ______________

17. Whom had God given to the Lord (v. 13)? ______________

____

18. Who had the power of death (v. 14)? ________________

19. By what means was this power destroyed (v. 14)? ________

20. What had the fear of death done to man (v. 15)? ________

____

21. Who is it who receives help (v. 16)? ________________

____

22. What office did the Lord take in things pertaining to God (v. 17)? ____

23. In this office, what was He to do (v. 17)? ______________

____

24. What qualified Him to help those who are tempted (v. 18).

____

DISCUSSION QUESTIONS

1. What is meant by "neglecting" salvation (v. 3)? How can one neglect salvation if he is aware of it? Is it possible to neglect salvation after one has accepted it? What would the punishment be for neglecting salvation? What procedures would you recommend for those who want to avoid this neglect?

2. What is the status of the human race in God's creation? Are all

human beings just a little lower than angels? If man was created this high, what happens after he sins? To what extent is he still in charge of all creation? How well do you think humanity is discharging its authority over God's works?

3. In what sense did Jesus taste of death for every person (v. 9)? How is it possible for Him to die for others; doesn't each one die for himself? What would this belief indicate about the nature of Jesus? If He died for every person, why do all people still suffer physical death? If He died for every person, wouldn't that death mean that all would be saved from death and none would be condemned?

4. In what respects was Jesus tempted (v. 18)? Can one be tempted without sinning? At what point does temptation turn into sin? What temptations do you think were the most difficult for Jesus to meet? Which do you think were easiest? If He had the supernatural powers which the New Testament attributes to Him, wouldn't it have been easy for Him to overcome temptation? How do you feel about Jesus' human qualities? Do you really feel that He understands your suffering and temptation?

5. How do you understand the references to the seed of Abraham (v. 16) in this letter addressed to the Hebrews? Did Jesus do anything for those who are Gentiles and not descended from Abraham? Can Jesus be a high priest to those who know nothing about the temple or the duties of priests? To what extent must non-Jews become children of Abraham in order to become brethren to the Lord (vv. 11, 12)? To what extent should Gentile Christians adopt Jewish practices such as circumcision, the keeping of the Ten Commandments, and the observance of Jewish holidays?

6. In what sense did Jesus become perfect through suffering (v. 10)? Wasn't He perfect already? Was He changed in some way after coming to earth and experiencing death? If He was changed, how can He have been one with God, for God cannot change (James 1:17)? Is there any sense in which we become perfect through suffering also? If so, how should we react to the suffering we experience? Should we ever ask God to heal us or to deliver us from suffering? How can we know whether suffering comes from God or from our own sin which results in punishment and suffering?

LESSON 3

Hebrews 3:1-19

CONTENT QUESTIONS

1. What positions of authority does Jesus hold (v. 1)? ________

____

2. In what respect was Jesus similar to Moses (v. 2)? ________

____

3. In what way was He different from Moses (v. 3)? ________

____

4. In what way was Moses like a house (v. 3)? ________

____

5. Who is the real Builder or Creator of all things (v. 4)?

____

6. If one thinks of Moses as a servant, how good a servant was he (v. 5)? ________

7. If Moses was a servant, who was Christ (v. 6)? ________

____

8. In this case, who are "we" (v. 6)? ________

9. Who was really speaking when the ancient writer wrote the Psalms (v. 7)? ________

10. What does God command in regard to "our" hearts (v. 8)?____

____

11. When was it that the fathers hardened their hearts (v. 8)?

12. How long had they seen God's works (v. 9)? ______________

13. How did God feel about those people (v. 10)? ______________

14. How often did their hearts go wrong (v. 10)? ______________

15. What oath did God take at this point (v. 11)? ______________

16. Of what were the brethren, the readers, to take heed (v. 12)? ______________

17. What were they to do for one another (v. 13)? ______________

18. If one keeps his confidence firm, what would be his relationship to Christ (v. 14)? ______________

19. What was the command that one would hear, in listening to God's voice (v. 15)? ______________

20. Who was it who disobeyed this command (v. 16)? ______________

21. During the forty years in the wilderness what happened to those who had sinned (v. 17)? ______________

22. To whom did God swear that they would not enter into His rest (v. 18)? ______________

23. What basic problem kept them out (v. 19)? ______________

DISCUSSION QUESTIONS

1. On the basis of what you know about Moses, what were his weaknesses in character? Was Jesus superior to him (v. 3) be-

cause of Moses' failures or because of Jesus' excellence? How would you compare Moses with other great leaders such as Abraham, Jacob, Joseph, Elijah, David, Daniel, or Isaiah? What are the qualities that make an individual great in God's sight?

2. Who were the "holy brethren" (vv. 1 and 12) whom the writer addresses in this chapter? What makes them "holy brethren"? Why is the writer so worried that they might "depart from the living God" (v. 12)? Why would he call them "brethren" if they were in danger of falling away? Was the writer concerned about all Christians or only about those who were half converted? What was missing in their faith that they needed to be warned like this?

3. How do you explain the actions of the Hebrews in their rebellion against Moses and against God in the wilderness? What caused the rebellion? Were they really conscious of rebelling against God? What were they thinking about? Do you see any of the same weaknesses and problems in the Christian fellowship today?

4. What did the writer have in mind when he asked the brethren to exhort or to encourage one another (v. 13)? What form do you think such encouragement should take? Do you feel that the Christians you know do an adequate job of encouraging others? What might your church be doing to offer such encouragement? What might you, as an individual, be doing?

5. What do you see in the picture of Christians as God's house (v. 6)? Should we understand this analogy in terms of our individual lives (see 1 Corinthians 6:19) or in terms of our corporate life (see Ephesians 2:21)? What teaching do you see here about the person and authority of Christ? What teaching do you see about our human nature? If your life is a house, would you say that God was the builder of all of it? Would you be willing to permit Jesus in all of its rooms? Are there aspects of life which we keep separate from our relationship to Christ? What makes us feel this way? What can we do about it?

6. What does this chapter teach about the nature of sin? In what sense is it deceitful (v. 13)? In what sense is it related to a hard heart (v. 8)? In what sense does it involve disobedience (v. 18)? Is sin basically a matter of a heart that goes wrong, or is it the overt act of disobedience? If sin begins in the heart, why isn't it

a sin to be tempted? In what respects do faith (v. 5) and boldness and hope (v. 6) serve to counteract sin? Is it possible for Christians today to live sinless lives? What can we do to reduce our tendency to sin?

LESSON 4

Hebrews 4:1-16

CONTENT QUESTIONS

1. What should a Christian fear (v. 1)? ______

______

2. What promise does the Christian have (v. 1)? ______

______

3. What had been preached to them (v. 2)? ______

4. Why were the ancients not profited by what they heard (v. 2)? ______

5. What happens to those who believe (v. 3)? ______

______

6. What did God swear in His anger (v. 3)? ______

______

7. What did God say about the seventh day (v. 4)? ______

______

8. Will all men enjoy a similar rest (v. 5)? ______

9. Will all men be prevented from entering this rest (v. 6)?

______

10. What prevented some of the ancients from finding rest (v. 6)? ______

11. What is one's obligation when he hears God speak (v. 7)?

______

12. Did the ancients, entering the promised land under Joshua, find any real rest (v. 8)? ______________________________

13. Who has the promise of a sabbath rest (v. 9)? ______________
____

14. When one finds rest, what example is he following (v. 10)?
____

15. What might prevent one from receiving this promise of rest (v. 11)? ______________________________

16. What is the Word of God like (v. 12)? __________________
____

17. What does the Word do (v. 12)? _____________________
____

18. How much does God know about mankind (v. 13)? ________
____

19. What picture of Jesus was the author presenting (v. 14)?
____

20. What did he see as the obligation of Jesus' followers, therefore (v. 14)? ______________________________

21. Did he regard Jesus as being truly understanding of the human condition (v. 15)? ______________________________

22. How should people react to all of this understanding (v. 16)?
____

DISCUSSION QUESTIONS

1. In what sense have Christians had "good news" preached to them (v. 2)? What was the nature of this news? Would it still be considered good news today? Does the average churchgoer today, who attends Sunday school and church, really hear any good news presented? Should our church meetings be oriented toward presenting the gospel or toward giving ethical instruction to those who already converted?

2. Why is it that the preaching of the good news does not always produce faith in those who hear? How do you understand the promise that faith comes from hearing the word (Romans 10:17)? If faith is not produced, who is at fault, the hearer or the preacher? What are some of the factors which operate to block the development of faith (see Matthew 13:18-23)? How did these factors operate in the experience of the ancient Hebrews? How do they operate in the experience of people today?

3. How do you explain God's anger (v. 3) over those who do not believe and who disobey? Is it literally true that people can make God angry? If God is eternal and unchanging (see James 1:17), how can any actions of people cause Him to become angry? Besides, doesn't God know ahead of time what people are going to do? Then why should their actions make Him angry? If God was angry at the ancient Hebrews, how do you suppose He feels toward modern Americans? If God is love (1 John 4:16), how can He be angry? Should our preaching today emphasize the love of God or the wrath of God?

4. What is the "sabbath rest" (v. 9) which remains for God's people? To what extent do we experience rest when we become Christians (Matthew 11:28, 29)? Is the author talking about a sabbath rest which God's people enjoy now or one which they will have in the future? In what respects do you think Heaven will be more restful than the ideal Christian life today? Do you think our church activities make the Christian life more restful, or are they designed to keep people from resting too much?

5. What did the author mean by the living "word of God" (v. 12)? Was he talking about a person or about the written Scriptures? If he was talking about the Scriptures, what writing do you think he had in mind? In what respect would this "word" be like a sword? How could it discern the thoughts and intents of the heart?

6. How do you understand the teaching that we have a high priest who has been tempted in all points (v. 15)? Is the idea of Jesus being a high priest really meaningful to modern non-Jews? How do you feel about Jesus being tempted? Does the idea tend to undermine His authority? What temptations do you think He experienced? Is there a danger that we might make Jesus too human and forget that He is also Lord?

LESSON 5

Hebrews 5:1-14

CONTENT QUESTIONS

1. Once a high priest had been taken from among men and appointed, what things concerned him (v. 1)? ______________

   ____

2. What were his duties (v. 1)? ______________________

   ____

3. How was he to feel about his people (v. 2)? ____________

   ____

4. How was he to think of himself (v. 2)? ______________

   ____

5. For whom did he need to make sacrifices for sins (v. 3)?

   ____

6. Who called or appointed the high priest (v. 4)? __________
7. Give an example of one high priest who was thus appointed (v. 4). ____________________________________
8. Give a second example of a high priest thus appointed (v. 5). ______________________________________
9. What is His relationship to God (v. 5)? ______________
10. How long is Christ to hold office (v. 6)? _____________
11. To what order of priests does He belong (v. 6)? _________
12. What sort of offerings did Christ make, in His days in the

flesh (v. 7)? ______

13. Why were His prayers heard (v. 7)? ______

______

14. What was it, in His earthly experience, by which the Son learned something about obedience (v. 8)? ______

______

15. What did the Son become, to those obeying Him (v. 9)? ______

______

16. Who named Him a high priest (v. 10)? ______

17. How difficult did the writer consider his message (v. 11)?

______

18. How bright did he consider his readers or listeners (v. 11)?

______

19. How far advanced should they have become in their studies of the oracles of God (v. 12)? ______

20. How far advanced had they become, in actuality (v. 12)? ______

______

21. If these listeners were regarded as children, what would have been the basic requirement of their diet (v. 12)? ______

______

22. What did their milk diet indicate about them (v. 13)? ______

______

23. Who could handle solid food (v. 14)? ______

24. What spiritual abilities would such people have (v. 14)?

______

DISCUSSION QUESTIONS

1. What qualifications did the writer expect the high priest to have? Should every church leader or minister be expected to have all

of these requirements today? Which do you think would be most important today? Which would be least important?

2. How is it possible for a priest to maintain high ethical standards while still being sympathetic with those who sin? Doesn't the sympathy also involve accepting the sin? How can the priest remind people of the ugly nature of sin while at the same time expressing love for the sinner? Would the sacrifices in the ancient temple have been helpful with this problem? How can Christians today reject the sin without rejecting the sinner?

3. How do you think people feel about priests or religious leaders who are themselves guilty of sin (v. 3)? Don't we expect our leaders to be sinless? To what extent is the church today full of hypocrites? If Christians are hypocritical, can we blame people for rejecting Christianity? If Christians don't live any better than other people, what difference does it make whether people become Christian or not?

4. What did Jesus learn from the suffering He experienced (v. 8)? If He knew all things, what more could he learn? If He was always obedient to God's will, how could He learn to be obedient? In what sense was suffering meaningful to Him? In what respects should suffering be meaningful to us? Is it really God's will that human beings should suffer? If God is loving and all-powerful, why does He permit suffering?

5. Why do you think the writer connected Jesus to Melchizedek (v. 6; see also Psalm 110:4 and Genesis 14)? Why didn't he connect Jesus to Aaron or to Levi? What did he gain by making Jesus a high priest? What would this picture add to the understanding of Jesus? Isn't it enough to understand Jesus as Messiah, as the King of Israel, as the Son of David? If you could talk to the author at this point, what questions would you raise which you would like him to answer as he continues the discussion?

6. How would you characterize your own spiritual maturity? To what extent are you able to digest solid spiritual food? How would you characterize the average Christian of your acquaintance in this regard? What would you recommend as the proper procedure to be followed in the local church to make Christians more mature?

LESSON 6

Hebrews 6:1-20

CONTENT QUESTIONS

1. What did the writer want his readers to do (v. 1)? ________

____

2. List two of the basic "foundations" which need not be laid again (v. 1). ________

____

3. List four more basic teachings which need not be repeated (v. 2). ________

____

____

4. Whose permission was needed in pressing ahead (v. 3)? ________

____

5. The author then spoke of another group of people. What had this group tasted (v. 4)? ________

6. Of what had they partaken (v. 4)? ________

7. Of what else had they tasted? ________

____

8. What is impossible for a Christian to do if he falls away completely (v. 6)? ________

9. What scene is reenacted (v. 6)? ________

____

10. What happens to land that brings forth a good crop (v. 7)?

____

11. What happens to land that brings forth thorns and thistles (v. 8)? ______________________________

12. Did the writer feel that his readers were like this bad land (v. 9)? ____________________________

13. What had these readers done (v. 10)? ________________

____

14. What did the writer desire for them (v. 11)? ______________

____

15. Whom did he want them to imitate (v. 12)? ______________

____

16. By whom did God swear to Abraham (v. 13)? ____________

17. What was God's promise to Abraham (v. 14)? ____________

____

18. What did Abraham do to obtain the promise (v. 15)? ________

____

19. According to the author, when men take oaths, by what do they swear (v. 16)? _________________________

20. When God took an oath, what was He trying to show to the heirs of His promise (v. 17)? ____________________

21. What should God's oath and God's promise encourage the readers to do (v. 18)? ________________________

22. What should this hope be for their souls (v. 19)? ___________

____

23. Where had Jesus entered as a forerunner or precursor (vv. 19, 20)? _______________________________

24. To what order of priesthood did Jesus belong (v. 20)? ______

____

DISCUSSION QUESTIONS

1. If you were telling Christians today to leave the basic things and press on to more advanced matters, what would you tell them to do? What should they study? What areas should they consider? How would you recommend they "press on to perfection" (v. 1)?

2. If you were making a list of the basic foundations of the faith for Christians today, what would you include? How would your list differ from the one given by the author (vv. 1, 2)? Is there anything you would omit from his list? Is there anything you would add?

3. To what extent should Christians try to imitate or to mimic other people (v. 12) such as Abraham? Is this a wise practice, in view of the fact that no human being is perfect? Wouldn't one be better advised to imitate Jesus rather than Abraham? What would one gain by imitating the lives of living Christians today? What would be the dangers? Should parents point to models like these in training their children?

4. What can one do in order to "minister unto the saints" (v. 10)? What form should such a ministry take today? What is the motive for such ministry? If salvation is not of works (Ephesians 2:8, 9), what is the purpose of such ministry? Isn't there a danger that Christians will come to think of such work as earning their salvation? Why did the author emphasize a ministry to the saints? Isn't a Christian supposed to minister to anyone in need?

5. What does the most to help Christians today to endure the trials of life patiently and to remain faithful (v. 15)? Which would be more effective, God's promises or our own subjective feelings? Can you name other factors which help Christians to endure? What factors do the most to discourage Christians and to tempt them to give up and to turn away? Do you think that your church is doing all it can to encourage endurance on the part of its members?

6. What do you think of expressions such as "king" and "high priest" (v. 20) as applied to Jesus? Are these terms meaningful

to us today? Is there any point in trying to give them meaning, or should we look for other expressions which would mean more to modern man? What does the term "priest" mean to you? Does it add anything to your understanding of Christ?

LESSON 7

Hebrews 7:1-28

CONTENT QUESTIONS

1. Who was Melchizedek (v. 1)? ______________________

2. What did Abraham give him (v. 2)? ______________________

3. What is known about Melchizedek's ancestors (v. 3)? ________

____

4. What did the author want his readers to consider about Melchizedek (v. 4)? ______________________

____

5. What had the sons of Levi, as priests, been commanded (v. 5)? ______________________

6. What did Melchizedek do for Abraham (v. 6)? ____________

____

7. Which is greater, one being blessed, or the one giving the blessing (v. 7)? ______________________

8. In what other respect was Melchizedek greater than the sons of Levi (v. 8)? ______________________

9. In what sense did Levi pay tithes (v. 9)? ______________________

____

10. When Melchizedek met Abraham, where was Levi (v. 10)? ___

____

11. What evidence did the author give that perfection was not

achieved through the Levitical priesthood (v. 11)? ________

____

12. If a priesthood is changed, what other change is necessary (v. 12)? ________

13. How many members of the tribe of Judah had served at the altar (vv. 13, 14)? ________

14. What had Moses said about priests from the tribe of Judah (v. 14)? ________

15. If another priest arose, who would he be like (v. 15)? ________

____

16. What would constitute the basis of his priesthood, if not the law or the commandments (v. 16)? ________

____

17. What did the Old Testament say about this priest (v. 17)?

____

18. Why would the previous commandments be cancelled or disannulled (v. 18)? ________

19. How many people did the law make perfect (v. 19)? ________

____

20. Name one other respect in which the new priest (Christ) is superior to the former priests (vv. 20, 21). ________

____

21. Of what, then, has Jesus become the surety or guarantor (v. 22)? ________

22. Why did the former covenant have so many priests (v. 23)?

____

23. Why is Jesus' priesthood unchangeable (v. 24)? ________

____

24. Why is Jesus so capable of saving those who come to Him (v. 25)? ______

25. According to the author, what is the nature of the high priest (v. 26)? ______

26. How many times did he offer sacrifices (v. 27)? ______

______

27. Why didn't this high priest offer continual sacrifices for himself (v. 28)? ______

______

DISCUSSION QUESTIONS

1. What do you see in this chapter in regard to the practice of paying tithes? If Abraham paid tithes to Melchizedek (v. 4), isn't the Christian today obligated to pay tithes to the Lord as high priest? Would you regard the payment of tithes as being a part of the new covenant?

2. In what respects did the author find parallels between Melchizedek and Christ (see vv. 2, 3)? Can you see any other points of similarity between these two that the author doesn't mention? Are there other Old Testament personalities that also show similarities to Christ? What do you think of this practice of comparing other people to Christ and finding "types" and pictures? Does it really help our understanding of Him?

3. What would you say was the essence of the covenant or agreement between God and the Hebrews? What is the essence of the agreement between God and Christians? What is each side of the agreement to do in each case? How do these covenants differ? How are they alike?

4. What characteristics of Jesus as our high priest can you find listed in this chapter? How do you feel about calling attention to these qualities? Do we need to think of Jesus as holy and separated from sinners? Is He more appealing as a human personality? Compare the picture here with the one found in Hebrews 4:15. Which appeals to you more? Which do you think is more needed in our day?

5. In what respects is the priesthood of Christ superior to the Levitical priesthood, according to the author? Do you think a modern Jew would find these arguments persuasive? What does this comparison of priestly orders indicate about the relationship between Christianity and Judaism? If we worship the same God through different orders of priests, aren't we basically the same religion? What do you think of the practice of having Jewish Rabbis speak in Christian churches?

6. How do you understand such Old Testament personalities as Melchizedek (Genesis 14:18), Jethro (Exodus 18:1-27), and Job (Job 1:1)? Where did these men get their knowledge of God? Who appointed them priests? Why do you think God chose Abraham rather than one of them to be father of a holy nation? Do you think there were others, not mentioned in the Bible, who were also followers of God? Are there similar followers today?

LESSON 8

Hebrews 8:1-13

CONTENT QUESTIONS

1. What is the main point that the author was making (v. 1)?

   ____

2. Where is the high priest (v. 1)? ______________________________

3. Where does this high priest minister (v. 2)? ______________________________

   ____

4. Who erected this tent or tabernacle (v. 2)? ______________________________

5. Why were high priests appointed (v. 3)? ______________________________

   ____

6. Therefore, what would this high priest need (v. 3)? ______________________________

   ____

7. If He were on earth, would He be a priest at all (v. 4)? ______________________________

   ____

8. On what basis did earthly priests make offerings (v. 4)? ______________________________

   ____

9. What was the relationship of their service to heavenly things (v. 5)? ______________________________

10. What warning was Moses given in building the tabernacle (v. 5)? ______________________________

11. How does the ministry of the new high priest compare with the old (v. 6)? ______________________________

12. How does the covenant that He mediates compare (v. 6)? ___

____

13. If the first covenant had been faultless, how long would it have lasted (v. 7)? ______________________

14. What did God promise about the covenant (v. 8)? ________

____

15. With whom would the new covenant be established (v. 8)? ___

____

16. When was the previous covenant made (v. 9)? ___________

____

17. How did the people respond to this covenant (v. 9)? _______

____

18. How did God react (v. 9)? _____________________

19. Where would the new laws be written (v. 10)? ___________

____

20. What would be the relationship of God and the people (v. 10)?

____

21. What teaching would not be necessary (v. 11)? ___________

____

22. Why would this teaching no longer be needed (v. 11)? _____

____

23. How did God promise to react to sins (v. 12)? ___________

____

24. What would the creation of a new covenant do to the old one (v. 13)? ______________________________

DISCUSSION QUESTIONS

1. Do human beings still need priests to offer gifts and sacrifices to God? Why can't each individual offer his own gifts and sacrifices? What makes people feel that priests are needed, thus giving rise to some sort of a priesthood in most religions? Is there any real basis for these feelings, or are they only superstitions? If Christians have Jesus as their high priest, do they have need for any other priests (see Revelation 1:6)?

2. Why do you think the author chose to write about the tabernacle rather than the temple which would have been so much more contemporary for his readers? Did he feel the tabernacle was more authentic? What, if anything, do you think this emphasis on the tabernacle indicates about the lesson he was trying to teach, about the time in which he wrote (before or after the destruction of the temple), about the place where his readers lived? Does this mention of the tabernacle have any significance for those of us living thousands of years after the destruction of both temple and tabernacle?

3. What were some of the faults (v. 7) of the old covenant? If God gave it, how could it be faulty? Why did God make an agreement which was less than perfect? What hope do you think Jeremiah and the Hebrew writer had that the second covenant would be any better than the first? As you look back over the past two thousand years, do you think the second covenant was better? If you could choose to live under the old covenant, would you do so?

4. Why does the new covenant omit teaching (v. 11)? Aren't Christians supposed to be witnesses, teaching and preaching to their neighbors (see Matthew 28:19, 20)? How do you understand what the writer says here in contrast to Hebrews 5:12? What should be the teaching ministry of the Christian community? How well do you think your church fulfills it?

5. How is it possible for God to forget sins and remember them no more (v. 12)? Can He ignore sins and still be a God of justice? How do you reconcile this promise with the principle that we reap what we sow? If God is willing to forget about sins, doesn't this fact encourage people to continue sinning? To what extent should we, as Christians, ignore sins in our relations with each

other? Can parents ignore sins and still teach proper conduct to their children?

6. What did the author mean by saying that the first covenant was vanishing away (v. 13)? Aren't the Ten Commandments eternal? Was he saying that we can live as we please without regard for the moral laws of God? If the ancient commandments disappear, what replaces them? Can you teach anything about sin and righteousness without using commandments of some sort?

7. What is the weakness of trying to change people by commandments and discipline? How does punishment affect those who do wrong? What should be the Christian way of changing lives? How should we apply these principles to lawless nations, to criminals, to young people who don't know any better?

LESSON 9

Hebrews 9:1-28

CONTENT QUESTIONS

1. What guided the worship or divine service of the first covenant (v. 1)? ______
2. What furniture did the tabernacle have (v. 2)? ______
3. What lay behind the second veil of the tabernacle (v. 3)? ______
4. What furniture did this room have (v. 4)? ______
5. What was the covering on top of the ark of the covenant (v. 5)? ______
6. Who conducted the services in the tabernacle (v. 6)? ______
7. Who was permitted to enter the second room, the Holy of Holies (v. 7)? ______
8. What was the Holy Spirit showing by this limited access to the Holy of Holies (v. 8)? ______
9. How effective were gifts and sacrifices in perfecting the worshiper (v. 9)? ______
10. How long would the system of gifts and sacrifices last (v. 10)? ______

11. When things were reformed, who became high priest (v. 11)?

____

12. What blood did He take into the Holy Place (v. 12)? ________

____

13. How effective was this blood (vv. 13, 14)? ______________

____

14. What did this blood accomplish for those wanting to serve God (v. 14)? ______________________________

15. What promise did the new covenant offer those who were called (v. 15)? ______________________________

16. What is required for a testament or will to be in effect (v. 16)? ______________________________

17. What was required for the dedication of the first covenant (v. 18)? ______________________________

18. What did Moses do with the blood (v. 19)? ______________

____

19. What did Moses say at this point (v. 20)? ______________

____

20. What else did he do (v. 21)? ______________________

____

21. According to the writer, what is the essential element in cleansing (v. 22)? ______________________________

22. When Christ made a better sacrifice, where did He go (v. 24)?

____

23. What did Christ sacrifice (v. 26)? ________________

24. What did the writer expect Christ to do in the future (v. 28)? ______________________________

DISCUSSION QUESTIONS

1. Why do you think the writer put the altar of incense with the furniture inside the Holy of Holies (v. 4) when it was actually outside (see Exodus 40:26)? What was he indicating about the altar of incense? If incense symbolizes prayer (see Revelation 5:8), what was he saying about prayer? If prayer should enter the Holy of Holies, why aren't our prayers more effective?

2. What do you think of the claim that Christianity is a bloody religion? Why did the Hebrew writer go to such lengths to tie the death of Christ (v. 12) to the ancient Jewish sacrifices? Was he merely trying to appeal to Jewish readers, or was he dealing with an essential aspect of Christianity? Can one become a Christian by accepting Jesus' ethical teachings without believing in a blood sacrifice? Isn't the idea that God demands blood sacrifice simply an old superstition? What evidence can you present that such ideas are important in the Christian religion (see Romans 6:3)?

3. If the high priest entering the Holy of Holies was a picture of Christ entering Heaven, what do you think the other parts of the tabernacle represented? What did the altar of incense represent? The table of shewbread? The candlestick or lampstand? The priest? The tabernacle itself?

4. In what sense does the sacrifice of Christ serve to cleanse the conscience (v. 14)? Does it make Christians forget the wrongs they have done? Should those becoming Christians forget all about their past sins? If so, wouldn't they escape the responsibility of trying to make restitution? Can the memory of past sins cause a handicap in Christian living? How can a Christian maintain a realization that he is a sinner without permitting these memories to damage his ability to serve God? Do other Christians have a responsibility to help with this problem?

5. Must the salvation of Christians actually wait until Christ comes back (v. 28)? Isn't the Christian saved now? In what sense is salvation still in the future? In what sense is it a present reality? Is it possible to be half-saved now and completely saved later on? Is it possible for one to become more "saved" day by day?

LESSON 10

Hebrews 10:1-39

CONTENT QUESTIONS

1. Can the law and its sacrifices make a worshiper perfect (v. 1)? ____________________
2. If a worshiper were perfect, what would be his consciousness of sin (v. 2)? ____________________
3. What did the sacrifices do with sin, year by year (v. 3)? ____________________
4. Why couldn't sacrifices remove sin (v. 4)? ____________________
5. Why did the Messiah come (v. 7)? ____________________
6. How did God feel about sacrifices (v. 8)? ____________________
7. What did the coming of the Messiah do to the system of sacrifices (v. 9)? ____________________
8. What then sanctified the worshiper (v. 10)? ____________________
9. What did Messiah do when He had finished the sacrifice (v. 12)? ____________________
10. What had His sacrifice accomplished (v. 14)? ____________________

11. Where is the law of the new covenant to be found (v. 16)?

____

12. How does the Lord now react to the sins of His people (v. 17)? ______________________________

13. How does one now enter the Holy Place (vv. 19, 20)? ______

____

14. List three things given by the writer that Christians ought to do (vv. 22-24).

    1. ______________________________

    2. ______________________________

    3. ______________________________

15. Give one thing that Christians should not do (v. 25). ________

____

16. If a Christian sinned willfully, what sacrifice remained for him (v. 26)? ______________________________

17. What, then, could he expect (v. 27)? ______________

____

18. What happened to one who broke Moses' law (v. 28)? ______

____

19. Would a Christian who sinned be better off (v. 29)? ________

____

20. How should such a one feel about God the Judge (v. 31)? __

____

21. What did the writer want his readers to remember (vv. 32, 33)?

____

22. How had they reacted to these problems (v. 34)? __________

____

23. How did the writer want them to react now (v. 35)? ________

____

24. What did they particularly need (v. 36)? ____________

____

25. How were they to live (v. 38)? ____________________

26. What was their faith going to bring about (v. 39)? ________

____

DISCUSSION QUESTIONS

1. Are Christians today overly conscious of their sins? What is the harm in remembering sins year by year (v. 3) or week by week? Does the average church service focus on the sin or on the forgiveness and freedom from sin? What about the hymns, the prayers, the sermon? Isn't there a danger that a Christian will become proud if he forgets that he was once a sinner (see 1 Corinthians 10:12)?

2. To what extent is the Christian to be like his Lord in doing the will of God (vv. 7 and 9)? How can we know what the will of God is in order to do it? What is our greatest handicap in doing God's will? How can we overcome it? What is the place of the local church in helping Christians to do God's will? Are there other sources of help that we might receive?

3. Why must Christ wait for His enemies to be destroyed (v. 13)? Why doesn't God destroy them at once? If God is all-powerful, why does He permit these enemies to continue? If He permits enemies like this, does He really care about us? What do you think would happen to mankind if God acted immediately to destroy His enemies?

4. How should Christians act today in order to follow the instructions of the writer to draw near (v. 22), to hold fast (v. 23), and to stimulate one another to good works (v. 24)? How is our assembling together (v. 25) related to these things? Is it possible for a Christian to do these things by himself? Why does he need to get involved with other Christians? To what extent must a Christian belong to a local church or fellowship of Christians? What should a missionary do if there is no assembly of Christians

available where he is living? Can he live the Christian life as effectively on the mission field by himself as he could at home with other Christians?

5. How do you understand the warnings about judgment given in verses 26-31 of this chapter? Does the writer mean that Christians who have once been saved may eventually be lost? Why is he so doubtful about the return of the backslider? Isn't it easier to restore a Christian who has sinned than it is to convert one who has never been a Christian at all? How would you explain what this writer says in the light of Galatians 6:1?

6. How did these Hebrew Christians feel about their possessions (v. 34)? How would you compare them to American Christians today in this regard? Do we depend too much on physical things? What would happen to modern Christians if they would be threatened with the loss of what they possess? What can be done today to help Christians rely more upon spiritual riches than upon material things?

7. What can be done to develop patience in a Christian, particularly the patience to remain faithful when times are difficult? Would you say that the Hebrew writer is effective in developing the patience of his readers? In what respects is he most effective? In what respects do you find him least effective? What can local churches do today to develop this patience in their membership?

LESSON 11

Hebrews 11:1-40

CONTENT QUESTIONS

1. How did the author define "faith" (v. 1)?

2. What do we believe, by faith, about the creation (v. 3)?

3. What did Abel do by faith (v. 4)?

4. What happened to Enoch because of his faith (v. 5)?

5. What must anyone believe who desires to come to God (v. 6)?

6. What did Noah do because of his faith (v. 7)?

7. When Abraham was called, what did he do (v.8)?

8. What did he become, because of his faith (v. 9)?

9. What unusual power did Sarah receive (v. 11)?

10. How much of the promises did these people receive (v. 13)?

11. How does God feel about them (v. 16)? ____________________

____

12. What did Abraham do by faith (v. 17)? ____________________

13. What did he think God would do (v. 19)? ____________________

____

14. What did Isaac do by faith (v. 20)? ____________________

____

15. What did Jacob do (v. 21)? ____________________

____

16. What commands did Joseph give (v. 22)? ____________________

____

17. What did their faith cause Moses' parents to do (v. 23)? ______

____

18. What did Moses, himself choose (vv. 24, 25)? ______________

____

19. Where did his faith lead him to live (v. 27)? ______________

20. What observance did Moses keep (v. 28)? ____________________

____

21. What city did faith destroy (v. 30)? ____________________

22. Name one who escaped this destruction (v. 31). ______________

23. Whose stories would the writer include if he had more time (v. 32)? ____________________

24. How effective is faith against lions (v. 33)? ______________

____

25. How effective is faith against death (v. 35)? ______________

____

26. Did the faithful ones of the past receive the fullness of

God's promises (v. 39)? ______________________________

27. What had God provided or foreseen beyond them (v. 40)? __

____

DISCUSSION QUESTIONS

1. How do you feel about the less admirable people who are found on this "roll of faith" in this chapter, people like Jacob, Rahab, Samson, Jephthah,and the like? (You may wish to look them up in the Old Testament to refresh your memory about their lives.) Are you surprised at the writer including them? Can you think of more admirable characters in the Old Testament whom he omits? Why do you think these were included? How do you think this list would compare with the roll of a modern church? Would members like these be accepted by our usual church congregation? Should Christians be willing to fellowship with such, or should we insist upon some changes?

2. How do you feel about the women on this list? Are they under-represented or over-represented in view of the accounts that we have in the Old Testament? How does their place on this list compare with their place in the average church of today? How do you feel about faithful women assuming places of leadership in the church?

3. What is the relationship between faith and strange events which seem to contradict natural law, including creation (v. 3), the power to conceive children (v. 11), the power to cross the sea (v. 29), and even power over death (v. 35)? Must one give up his belief in natural law to have faith? Which is more important, to be willing to sacrifice everything for one's principles or to hold a belief in the supernatural? Can one have the faith that this writer recommends without believing in supernatural miracles?

4. What new insights are found in this chapter that add to what we know in the Old Testament? For example, if Abel (v. 4) offered a better sacrifice than Cain through faith, what would this fact indicate about the instructions the two men must have received (see Genesis 4:3-5)? How did Moses (v. 27) feel about the king's anger when he left Egypt (see Exodus 2:15)? Can you find other examples?

5. To what extent should a Christian, today, feel like a "pilgrim" and "stranger" (v. 13) in his life on this earth? Is it necessary for us, in modern times, to feel that we don't really belong here in order to be people of faith? If so, how would you evaluate your life and the lives of people you know in terms of their "other-world" orientation? Do we handle money, time, possessions, and the like as though we are strangers here, looking for another homeland?

6. In what sense did these faithful people of past ages fail to receive God's promise (v. 39)? In what sense are they made perfect in company with the people of the writer's day? Would you say that first century Christians received God's promise and were made perfect, or do they also require the Christians of the past two thousand years? In what respects do Christians require one another in order to be made perfect and to receive the fullness of God's promises?

LESSON 12

Hebrews 12:1-29

CONTENT QUESTIONS

1. What did the author want his listeners to do (v. 1)? ________

   ______________________________ and ____________________

   ____

2. Where is Jesus now (v. 2)? _______________________________

   ____

3. How hard had his readers struggled against sin, according to the author (v. 4)? ____________________________

   ____

4. What pieces of instruction had they tended to forget (vv. 5, 6)? ____

   ____

5. In actuality, how was God treating them (v. 7)? ___________

   ____

6. If their lives were too easy, what might it prove (v. 8)?

   ____

7. What should be their attitude toward God (v. 9)? __________

   ____

8. What was God trying to accomplish in their hardships (v. 10)? ____

9. What good comes out of chastening (v. 11)? ______________

   ____

10. How did the writer want his readers to react (vv. 12, 13)?

____

11. What is required to see the Lord (v. 14)? ________________

12. Whom did the writer specify as a bad example (v. 16)? ____

____

13. How hard did Esau try to change his father's mind (v. 17)?

____

14. How did Mount Sinai appear to the ancient Israelites (vv. 18, 19)? ______________________________________

15. What happened to a beast that touched the mountain (v. 20)?

____

16. How did Moses feel about the mountain (v. 21)? __________

____

17. To what mountain were the Hebrew Christians coming (v. 22)?

____

18. To what persons were they coming (vv. 22-24)? ___________

____

19. How did the writer describe Jesus (v. 24)?________________

____

20. What command did the writer give (v. 25)?________________

____

21. What promise or warning did he cite (v. 26)? ______________

____

22. If those things shaken were removed, what would remain (v. 27)? ______________________________________

23. How should people serve God (v. 28)?___________________

____

24. According to this writer, what is the nature of God (v. 29)?

____

DISCUSSION QUESTIONS

1. Do you think the writer is correct in his view of problems, hardships, and persecutions? Do these represent God's chastening (v. 6)? Do troubles always indicate that one is a true son of God (v. 7)? Would an easy life demonstrate that one is not a true son (v. 8)? Would these principles hold true in modern society? If you evaluated Christians today on the basis of their troubles, would they have more difficult lives than non-Christians? If so, why should one become a Christian? Are there dangers in trying to sell Christianity on the basis of rewards in this life?

2. What is your reaction to the picture of God found in this chapter? How would you reconcile this understanding with the idea that God is love? Do you think Jesus would have approved of the teaching found here? What understanding of God is most needed in our day, by the world, by the church, in your own life?

3. Do you think the dead literally witness what goes on among the living? Are they conscious, or do they sleep until the resurrection day? What did the author have in mind in calling them "witnesses" (v. 1)? If they literally witnessed our acts and our failures, would they be happy? Do you find it encouraging to think of these witnesses of the past watching you?

4. What are some of the "weights" which hinder us from running as Christians (v. 1)? What is the difference between weights and sins? Which is easier to identify? Which is easier to eliminate? In your own case, which weight gives you the most difficulty? Which do you think is most common among Christians of our day?

5. What did the writer mean by urging his readers to follow after sanctification of holiness (v. 14)? If they were looking unto Jesus (v. 2) and if God was dealing with them as sons (v. 7), were they already saved and therefore holy? What need did they have for further sanctification? Why was further holiness required for them to see the Lord? How holy does God expect His

people to be? If we are required to be holy in order to see God, does our salvation then depend on our own works rather than upon God's grace (see Ephesians 2:8, 9)?

6. How can bitterness or sin on the part of one member serve to trouble or defile the whole body of believers (v. 15)? Aren't we individually responsible for our own sins? In what respects do the sins of others affect us? If we have a mutual responsibility at this point, how should the local church act in the discipline of its members?

7. What do you think of Esau as an example of a profane person? (Review the story in Genesis 25:27-34.) Is the writer using Esau as a warning to readers who are saved, or is he speaking to non-Christians? Is it possible today for people to turn away from God so that they cannot turn around, even though they bitterly regret what they have done? Is repentance always possible, so long as one is alive?

LESSON 13

Hebrews 13:1-25

CONTENT QUESTIONS

1. What feelings, on the part of his readers, did the writer want continued (v. 1)? ______
2. Why should they show love to strangers (v. 2)? ______
3. What people were they to remember (v. 3)? ______
4. What sins particularly call for God's judgment (v. 4)? ______
5. How should they feel about money (v. 5)? ______
6. Who would be their source of help (v. 6)? ______
7. How should they act toward those who had brought God's word to them (v. 7)? ______
8. How changeable is Jesus (v. 8)? ______
9. How should they react to new and strange teachings (v. 9)? ______
10. What restriction did the writer mention as to the food of those serving the tabernacle (v. 10)? ______

11. What happened to the bodies of animals killed in sacrifice (v. 11)? ______

12. Where was Jesus when he suffered (v. 12)? ______

______

13. Therefore, where did the writer instruct his readers to go (v. 13)? ______

14. What city were they seeking (v. 14)? ______

______

15. What sacrifice should they continue to offer (v. 15)? ______

______

16. How would God feel about such sacrifices (v. 16)? ______

______

17. Whom should they obey (v. 17)? ______

18. For whom should they pray (v. 18)? ______

19. Where did the writer expect to go, in answer to their prayers (v. 19)? ______

20. What had God done for the Lord Jesus (v. 20)? ______

______

21. What did the writer want God to do for his readers (v. 21)?

______

22. Who should receive the glory for all this (v. 21)? ______

______

23. How long a letter did the writer feel he had written (v. 22)? ______

24. What had happened to Timothy (v. 23)? ______

______

25. Who else sent greetings (v. 24)? ______

DISCUSSION QUESTIONS

1. What is involved in showing love to strangers (v. 2)? What did the writer have in mind in his mention of entertaining angels (see Genesis)? Why did the writer refer to such incidents? Is the command to love enough by itself? Can one really love if he does it for a selfish motive? What can churches do today to encourage the love of strangers?

2. What do you think of the standard of sexual morality demanded by this writer (v. 4)? Was he expecting too much of his readers? How can Christians demand such high standards without driving away those who are tempted by these sins? Is there a danger that Christians will reject the sinner while attacking the sin?

3. The writer warns against three sins in verses 2-5; these are essentially the sins of pride, lust, and greed. Would the same warning still be necessary in a letter to Christians of our day? Do you think the temptations in these areas are as bad in modern times as they were in ancient times? Which of the three areas do you see as most dangerous to modern Christians? Which is most dangerous in your own life? What should the church be doing to protect individual members in these areas?

4. How should a Christian feel about those who "rule" over him in the church, his "leaders" in the faith (vv. 7, 17)? Would the author have approved of the way your church treats its minister? How do you think the writer would have regarded a paid clergy? How should a Christian handle the situation where church leaders seem to be in error in their teachings? Should one obey teaching which is wrong? How can one be obedient and submissive (v. 17) while at the same time maintaining the purity of the doctrine? Is there a danger of the sin of pride in those cases where a Christian sets up his interpretations in opposition to the teachings of church leaders?

5. What should be the Christian teaching about food and dieting (v. 9)? Was the author really objecting to food regulations, or was he merely trying to turn his readers away from Judaism? Should the church try to legislate the diets of its members, restricting certain foods or drinks? Should the church try to legislate in regard to alcoholic beverages? Does the Christian have an obligation to remain in good health and to avoid those things

which tend to damage the body? Does the church as a whole have a responsibility to its members in these areas?

6. Why does the writer request the prayers (v. 18) of his readers? If they were immature (5:12) and in danger of God's judgment (10:29), shouldn't they pray for themselves? How could their prayers result in his being restored to them sooner? If his life was going according to God's plan and if God's will for him was best, why should he ask that the plan be changed? Is a Christian better advised to accept God's will rather than praying to change it? What is the purpose of prayer? What would praying do for these people?

LESSON 14

James 1:1-27

CONTENT QUESTIONS

1. How did James describe himself (v. 1)? ____________________

 ____

2. To whom was he writing (v. 1)? ____________________
3. How should one feel about temptation (v. 2)? ____________________
4. What should result from the testing or proving of one's faith (v. 3)? ____________________
5. What did James see as the ultimate objective (v. 4)? ____________________

 ____

6. How could one find wisdom (v. 5)? ____________________
7. To what did he compare a doubter (v. 6)? ____________________

 ____

8. Should a doubter expect anything from the Lord (v. 7)? ____________________

 ____

9. How did the writer advise a Christian of the poor, lower class to feel (v. 9)? ____________________
10. To what did James compare the rich (vv. 10, 11)? ____________________

 ____

11. What was promised to one enduring temptation (v. 12)? ____________________

 ____

12. Why should one not blame temptation on God (v. 13)? ____________________

 ____

13. What causes temptation (v. 14)? ____________________

14. What could result from sin (v. 15)? ____________________

15. Who gave good and perfect things (v. 17)? ____________________

16. What was God's plan in creating mankind (v. 18)? ____________

____

17. In what respects should a person be slow (v. 19)? ____________

____

18. How should one receive the Word which leads to salvation (v. 21)? ____________________

19. Would it ever be enough to hear the Word only (v. 22)? ______

____

20. If one heard without doing, what would he be like (vv. 23, 24)? ____________________

21. What was promised for the one who acted as well as heard (v. 25)? ____________________

22. If one would be truly religious, what part of the body should he control (v. 26)? ____________________

23. How did James define pure religion (v. 27)? ____________

____

DISCUSSION QUESTIONS

1. Why should temptation be a time of joy? Is being tempted a sign that one is spiritually weak? Does temptation present hardships which could cause sorrow rather than joy? Does temptation tend to destroy faith rather than strengthen it? To what extent should we share our temptations with others in order to receive their help in time of testing? What is the place of the church fellowship in helping individuals who are being tempted?

2. What is the real source of temptation? If God does not tempt us, why should we pray "lead us not into temptation" (Matthew 6:13)? Should we look for the source of temptation in ourselves

or in some sort of personal devil? If the devil does not tempt us, how do you explain the temptations of Jesus (Matthew 4:1-11)? If temptation originates with the devil, is the responsibility with him when we fall to the temptation? To what extent should one feel personally guilty about falling to temptation and sinning?

3. What is the difference between wisdom and knowledge? Does God give knowledge if we ask for it? Can one have wisdom without knowledge? What is the responsibility of the educational program of the church? How effective is our church in its education of youth?

4. How can one live without doubts coming into his mind? Is a real life of faith possible for the Christian? What can we do to stimulate and to exercise our faith to eliminate our doubts? What is our mutual responsibility to build faith in one another?

5. What is the Christian attitude toward riches? Does Jesus' advice to the rich young ruler (Matthew 19:16-22) apply to rich people today? Is the average American Christian rich or poor in comparison to the other people of the world? What is the American's responsibility toward these others? How much of that responsibility can be assumed by the government? What can we as individuals do that our government is not doing?

6. If God is the source of the good things we receive (v. 17), then where do the evil things come from? If God is without change or variation, how could He have anything to do with evil? If evil exists apart from God, how can God be the Creator of all things?

7. Which is the more important aspect of religion, to do good to others or to keep one's self unspotted by the world (v. 27)? Where should we place the emphasis in our day? Does your church emphasize social service or personal holiness? Which do you personally find easiest? Most difficult?

8. If a person is to be a "doer" as a Christian (v. 22), what should he be doing? Should his actions aim at the relief of human suffering or the spreading of the Christian faith? Is it possible to do one without the other? Which should receive the highest priority?

LESSON 15

James 2:1-26

CONTENT QUESTIONS

1. What were Christians told to do about holding their faith in respect to persons (v. 1)? ____________________

____

2. What might they have said to a rich, well dressed man (v. 3)? ____________________

3. What might they have said to a poor, ragged fellow (v. 3)?

____

4. In what way would this treatment of people reflect upon themselves (v. 4)? ____________________

5. How had God treated the poor (v. 5)? ____________________

____

6. How had the rich treated these Christians (v. 6)? ____________________

____

7. What would their discrimination do to the name of Christ (v. 7)? ____________________

8. What law should they be following (v. 8)? ____________________

____

9. In what respect would they be sinning (v. 9)? ____________________

____

10. If one only broke a minor commandment, how guilty would he be (v.10)? ____________________

11. How much of the law has a murderer broken (v. 11)? ______

____

12. According to James, what law would judge his readers (v. 12)? ____

13. Which is more important, mercy or judgment (v. 13)? ______

____

14. If a man claimed to have faith, what more did he need (v. 14)? ____

15. If a brother lacked food, what should one do about it (vv. 15, 16)? ____

16. What makes faith truly alive (v. 17)? ______________

17. How can one show his faith (v. 18)? ______________

18. If one believes in God, does that faith make him a saint (v. 19)? ____

19. What is the nature of faith apart from works (v. 20)? ______

____

20. How was Abraham justified (v. 21)? ______________

____

21. What can works do for one's faith (v. 22)? ______________

____

22. What was Abraham's relationship to God (v. 23)? ______

____

23. What can works do for a person (v. 24)? ______________

24. How was Rahab justified (v. 25)? ______________

____

25. If faith is separated from works, what happens to it (v. 26)? ____

DISCUSSION QUESTIONS

1. What are some of the factors which cause discrimination in modern society? Do we still separate people for economic reasons like these ancient Christians? Which factors do you consider the most harmful to Christian relationships? Do you find any of these factors operating within your congregation? If so, what can be done about it?

2. How should the Christian citizen act in regard to segregation and discrimination in American political and social life? In particular, what position should the Christian take in regard to the following:
   A. Racially segregated housing?
   B. School busing to integrate the public schools?
   C. Attempts to remove Christian symbols and obervances from public educational and political gatherings?
   D. Sexual discrimination in employment?
   E. Pressure to remove the teaching of evolution or items critical of religion from school textbooks?
   F. Labor contracts requiring union membership of all employees in a plant or industry?
   G. "Affirmative action" procedures to achieve racial balance in employment?

3. Do you agree with James that the breaking of one commandment makes one guilty of breaking the whole law (v. 10)? If so, why do we try to distinguish between the seriousness of various sins? Is a "little white lie," told in order to be kind, just as bad as a deliberate lie told in order to destroy another person? Is adultery really serious if the man and woman love each other and her marriage was breaking up anyway? Is manslaughter as bad as murder? Why did James fail to mention the motive involved in the breaking of the law? Is stealing bread to help a starving family as bad as stealing money to get rich? Is the motive and the situation basic to understanding sin? Would it really be "adultery" (v. 11), if two people were expressing genuine love for one another (v. 8)?

4. How do you understand James' statement that works are necessary to one's justification (v. 24)? Was James contradicting the teachings of Paul, for example, in Galatians 3:1-5? If salvation is by works, does it depend on ourselves rather than on God? If

our works save us, should we be proud of what we have accomplished (see Ephesians 2:8, 9)? What do you think about the emphasis placed on works, as opposed to faith in the teaching and ministry of modern churches?

5. Was James contradicting the teachings of Jesus in regard to belief, for example John 11:26? Is one who believes on Jesus saved instantly at the moment of his belief, or must he wait to prove his faith by good works? If one is instantly saved, how do you explain these teachings of James? If one must wait, how do you explain Jesus' words to the thief on the cross (Luke 23:43)?

LESSON 16

James 3:1-18

CONTENT QUESTIONS

1. What profession should a Christian avoid (v. 1)? ____________

____

2. Why did James express this warning (v. 1)? ____________

____

3. In what respect is a Christian most likely to stumble (v. 2)? ____________

4. How much of a horse does the bridle control (v. 3)? ________

____

5. How is a ship controlled (v. 4)? ____________

6. Is the tongue's boasting in keeping with its size (v. 5)?

____

7. What does the tongue do for the entire body (v. 6)? ________

____

8. If the tongue is a fire, where does it get its flame (v. 6)?

____

9. How successful has man been at taming wild creatures (v. 7)?

____

10. How successful has man been at taming his tongue (v. 8)? ____

____

11. What does the tongue do in regard to God (v. 9)? ________

____

12. What does the tongue do in regard to man (v. 9)? ________

____

13. How did James feel about these contrary words (v. 10)? ____

____

14. In what respect did he find a mouth like a fountain (v. 11)?

____

15. In what respect did he find a mouth like a fig tree (v. 12)?

____

16. How can one demonstrate his wisdom (v. 13)? ________

____

17. What are the instructions for those with jealous or selfish hearts (v. 14)? ________________

____

18. What is the nature of the wisdom that did not come from above (v. 15)? ________________

19. When James saw jealousies and divisions, what else did he expect to follow (v. 16)? ________________

____

20. How does he describe the wisdom from above (v. 17)? ____

____

21. What were the peacemakers doing (v. 18)? ____________

____

DISCUSSION QUESTIONS

1. Why was James so critical of the tongue (v. 8)? Did he know that the tongue expresses what is in the heart (Matthew 15:18)? Does the tongue sometimes say things which the person does not intend? Where would you locate the control center of the personality? Are we influenced by forces outside ourselves (v. 6)?

2. What does it take for a person to gain control over his words (v. 2)? How can parents help their children gain such control? What is our mutual responsibility toward others in this respect? Is it proper to establish laws to control what people say? Should freedom of speech be absolute, or should society control communication which is slanderous? How much freedom of expression should be permitted to companies advertising their products? What is the responsibility of local churches in teaching responsibility in this area to individual members?

3. Why did James warn against the teaching profession (v. 1)? Do teachers receive a heavier judgment? Should teachers be held responsible for what students do or fail to do? Does the average Christian today need this warning? Does advice like this make it difficult to obtain the necessary teachers for church instruction? What can be done to recruit and train able teachers to Christianity? What can be done to eliminate unqualified teachers from the profession?

4. How would you compare the two types of wisdom that James mentioned (vv. 15, 17)? In what respects are the two different? In what respects are they alike? Why did James use the word "wisdom" to describe the bitter, jealous, earthly turn of mind (v. 15)? Why didn't he mention knowledge or learning as a part of either type of wisdom? Would the ideal Christian, fitting James' description, be regarded as wise by most people today?

5. Compare James' list of virtues with Paul's list found in Galatians 5:22, 23. What qualities are listed by both? What qualities are omitted by one or the other? How do you explain the differences? Compare Paul's list of the works of the flesh (Galatians 5:19-21, 26) with the list given by James (vv. 14-16). How do you explain these differences?

6. What should be the Christian standard for purity of language? Should one use the Lord's name as an expression of strong feeling? Should one use substitutes like "gosh" or "darn"? Should one ever curse or condemn people (v. 10)? Should one curse or condemn things or situations? If one feels these emotions and doesn't express them, is he harming himself? Is he being hypocritical (v. 17)? How can we train our children in habits of clean speech?

LESSON 17

James 4:1-17

CONTENT QUESTIONS

1. Where did wars originate, according to James (v. 1)? ______

____

2. Why didn't the Christians receive more of the good things of life (v. 2)? ______________________________
3. What were some of the sins of these people (v. 2)? ________

____

4. When they asked for things, what did they intend to do with what they received (v. 3)? ______________________________

____

5. What was the relationship with God of those who were friendly to the world (v. 4)? ______________________________
6. If one made himself a friend of the world, what did he do to his relationship to God (v. 4)? ______________________
7. What advice did the Scripture give on these matters (v. 5)?

____

8. What did the Scripture warn about those who were proud (v. 6)? ______________________________
9. What did the Scripture promise the humble (v. 6)? ________

____

10. To whom should the Christian be subject (v. 7)? ___________

____

11. Whom should the Christian resist (v. 7)? ____________________

12. What will happen if one draws close to God (v. 8)? __________

____

13. What should the sinner do with his hands (v. 8)? ___________

____

14. What should he do with his heart (v. 8)? ___________________

____

15. What should be his emotions at this point (v. 9)? ___________

____

16. If he humbles himself, what will God do (v. 10)? ___________

____

17. If one speaks against or judges his brother, what will he really be doing (v. 11)? _____________________________________

____

18. What sort of a person was one who spoke against or judged the law (v. 11)? ____

19. Who was the real lawgiver (v. 12)? _________________________

____

20. What common saying did James question (v. 13)? ____________

____

21. What was the true fact in regard to this saying (v. 14)?______

____

22. What was the real nature of their lives (v. 14)?_____________

____

23. What should they have said (v. 15)? ______________________

____

24. What was the real nature of their thinking (v. 16)? __________

____

25. If one knows the good and fails to do it, what is the nature of his failure (v. 17)? ______________________

____

DISCUSSION QUESTIONS

1. How do you feel about James' analysis of the causes of fightings and wars? Do the same causes result in wars in modern times? Was James talking about relationship between people, or would his words fit international relationships as well? To what extent do his words apply to non-Christians, or do they fight for additional reasons? What would James offer as the solution to the problem of war? Do you agree?

2. What do you think James would advise the oppressed people of our world, those who are denied basic needs for food and clothes because of race or family or economic conditions? Would James talk to them about peace or humility? Does one have a right to act against the oppressor in order to gain a better life for one's self and one's family? Were our ancestors right in fighting for their independence from Britain? If so, are the colonial people of Africa or South America equally right in demanding freedom today? What should be the response of Christianity in the face of these demands? How do you think James would view them?

3. Is it true today that we don't receive because we don't ask (v. 2)? Are we asking for more and more all the time? What should we be asking that we overlook? Do you agree that even when we ask, we don't ask in the right way (v. 3)? Which is our greatest problem, not asking or not asking in the right way? What can we do to help our children avoid these difficulties?

4. What do you think of pleasure as a guiding principle of life (v. 3)? Should the Christian ever seek pleasure for himself? If not, should the Christian seek pain or discomfort as his guiding principle? All good things come from God (James 1:17). Is human pleasure a good thing? If God wants us to be happy, then wouldn't He approve of those things that make us happy? When is it that pleasure becomes an evil guide? Under what circumstances is it wrong?

5. How does one resist the devil? How does one recognize the devil in the first place? Is he an actual personality or merely a combination of evil forces? Once we identify the evil, how do we resist? Which is more difficult, to recognize the evil which attracts us or to resist the attraction once we know it?

6. How do we draw near to God (v. 8)? What are some of the things which help us in these efforts? Is the primary responsibility upon us to draw near, or is it on God to draw us near? Does drawing near to God help us in resisting the devil? To what extent does the person who stays near God avoid temptation?

7. What's wrong with saying what we intend to do (v. 13)? Would James want us to plan for the future? How would he feel about buying insurance? Would it solve the problem if we say "be the good Lord willing" (v. 15) whenever we talk about the future? If such a formula improves our Christian living, are we in danger of reducing the faith to certain magic words?

LESSON 18

James 5:1-20

CONTENT QUESTIONS

1. What advice did James give the rich people (v. 1)? ________

____

2. What was the state of their possessions (vv. 2, 3)? ________

____

3. What would their money do to them (v. 3)? ________

____

4. What were these rich people doing to their hired workers (v. 4)? ________

5. Who was listening to the workers' complaints (v. 4)? ________

____

6. What sort of a living did these rich people have (v. 5)? ________

____

7. Of what crime were they guilty (v. 6)? ________

____

8. How long were Christians to be patient (v. 7)? ________

____

9. Who should serve as an example to them (v. 7)? ________

____

10. What event did James regard as being at hand (v. 8)? ________

____

11. What behavior were they to avoid, since judgment was so near (v. 9)? ____________________

12. Who else was to be an example for them (v. 10)? ____________________

____

13. What had the Lord finally shown about himself in His treatment of Job (v. 11)? ____________________

____

14. What sort of talk were these Christians commanded to avoid (v. 12)? ____________________

15. What should one do in suffering (v. 13)? ____________________

16. What should one do when cheerful (v. 13)? ____________________

17. What should the elders do when called to help the sick (v. 14)? ____________________

18. List two things the Lord would do for the sick (v. 15). ____________________

____

and ____________________

19. List two things Christians should do for one another (v. 16). ____________________

and ____________________

20. What happened when Elijah prayed (v. 17)? ____________________

____

21. What happened when he prayed again (v. 18)? ____________________

____

22. List two things accomplished by one who turns a sinner from the error of his ways (vv. 19, 20). ____________________

____________________ and ____________________

DISCUSSION QUESTIONS

1. How would James feel about wealthy people today? Was he concerned about their dishonesty, or did he object to their many possessions and their easy life? How would he feel about the ordinary American Christian with two cars, a television set, and all the appliances in the kitchen? Should Americans feel guilty about all their possessions in view of the needs of the rest of the world? To what extent should we send food to hungry people around the world when such giving makes food scarce for us?

2. What is your own feeling about the long-delayed return of Christ? Why did God permit writers like James to expect an early return if the return was to be so long delayed? Should we expect an early return today? If the whole thing is so uncertain, should we omit it from the preaching and teaching in our modern churches? How should we approach the portions of the New Testament that deal with the subject of the second coming?

3. Is the virtue of patience needed as badly today as it was in James' time? How would you compare it with such qualities as love, joy, and peace? What things cause you to be impatient? What can we do, in our homes and in our churches, to encourage the development of patience?

4. What did James mean by "let your yea be yea; and your nay, nay" in verse 12? Was he talking about speech habits or about keeping one's word? Which is more important, avoiding improper or impolite language, or doing what you say you are going to do? How would James feel about a witness taking an oath in court? To what extent is the word of the average person to be trusted in business or in society? Is the Christian better than the average? What do you think should be done to lead Christians to higher standards in this area? How can parents lead children to value the sanctity of their word?

5. What do you think about the practice of divine healing? Why did James give these instructions about anointing with oil (v. 14)? Why didn't Jesus and the apostles anoint with oil when they healed? (See Mark 6:13 for the exception.) Was James' primary concern with the healing of the body or with the forgiveness of sins? Do divine healers today actually heal the body, or do they merely overcome psychological problems? To what extent

should modern churches organize a healing ministry? What form should such a ministry take?

6. Are Christians today expected to confess sins to each other (v. 16)? To whom should sins be confessed? Should churches have a regular procedure for confessions? If forgiveness comes from God, shouldn't sins be confessed to God? Why should we involve anyone else?

7. How do you explain James' statement about saving a soul from death if one turns a wandering brother from error (v. 20)? Was the brother really in danger of spiritual death? Would the Lord hold such a one eternally secure (John 10:28)? How could the help of such a sinner serve to cover a multitude of sins (v. 20)? Whose sins would these be? In what sense would they be covered?

LESSON 19

1 Peter 1:1-25

CONTENT QUESTIONS

1. What was the status of the writer (v. 1)? ____________________
2. To what provinces was he sending the letter (v. 1)? __________

   ____________________ , ____________________

   ______________ , ______________ , ______________
3. What did the writer wish for his readers (v. 2)? ____________

   ____
4. What had God done which offered a living hope to man (v. 3)? ____
5. What was the nature of the inheritance being offered to man (v. 4)? ____
6. When would man's salvation finally be revealed (v. 5)? ______

   ____
7. How did the readers feel about this hope for salvation (v. 6)? ____
8. What would be the result of their trials when Jesus Christ is finally revealed (v. 7)? ______________________

   ____
9. How did they feel about Jesus Christ (v. 8)? ______________

   ____
10. What did Peter promise they would receive as a

result of their faith (v. 9)? ______

11. What had the prophets prophesied about these people (v. 10)?

______

12. What had the prophets testified beforehand about Christ (v. 11)? ______

13. How had these Christians learned about all these things (v. 12)? ______

14. On what were they to set their hope (v. 13)? ______

______

15. What had been the nature of their previous lives, when they were ignorant of these things (v. 14)? ______

______

16. What sort of lives were they to live henceforth (vv. 15, 16)?

______

17. What should be their feelings as time passed by (v. 17)? ______

______

18. List some things which had not redeemed them (v. 18). ______

______

19. What had redeemed them (v. 19)? ______

______

20. How long before had the coming of Christ been planned (v. 20)? ______

21. What had God done to the Christ (v. 21)? ______

______

22. How should these people feel about one another (v. 22)? ______

______

23. What had been the instrument of their being born again

(v. 23)? ______________________________

24. How permanent did Peter claim God's Word to be (vv. 24, 25)?

____

DISCUSSION QUESTIONS

1. Why do you think Peter wrote to these people about a salvation in the future, an inheritance reserved in Heaven for them (vv. 4, 5)? Is salvation something Christians can enjoy immediately? What immediate benefits was Peter overlooking? Would Christianity be worthwhile if it pertained only to this life and offered nothing after death? Do you think we make a mistake when we witness to people telling them about a "pie in the sky by and by"? What should be our emphasis? Which aspect of salvation, present or future, do you find most attractive?

2. How do you like Peter's approach to these people in their time of trial and testing? Is this the kind of thing that you would appreciate if you were ill, in need of food or clothing or shelter, or rejected by other people? What would you suggest might be added in trying to help people through difficult times today? What is the responsibility of individual Christians in offering this help to their fellows? To what extent should Christians turn this responsibility over to a professional minister?

3. Which do you think is easier, to have seen Jesus in the flesh and believe on Him, or to believe on Him without having seen Him in the flesh (v. 8)? If "seeing is believing," how do you explain the great number who saw Him and did not believe? If we do not see Him, what is to prevent us from believing in an imaginary Jesus, created to suit ourselves, who never existed at all?

4. When Peter commanded his readers to be "holy" (vv. 15, 16), what did he have in mind? Is the quality of holiness basically what one does or what one refrains from doing; is it a positive or a negative thing? What do you think Peter saw as being different about the life-style of holy Christians in those days? What would be the difference today?

5. What is the basic source of power in living the Christian life? Does it come from one's own efforts (vv. 13, 14, 22) or from God's help (Romans 8:13, 26). Why are some Christians more

saintly than others? How can we develop such qualities as love within ourselves? What can churches do to encourage their members to Christian living? What can parents do in preparing their children to live holy lives?

6. How would you define the sense of fear or awe that people should have toward God (v. 17)? If God is our Father, why should we be in awe of Him? If He is the almighty Judge, how can we love Him as Father? What understanding of God is most needed today by people in general, by Christians, and by the members of the church to which you belong? What would you suggest might be done to restore the proper balance in their understanding?

7. How does one develop the kind of Christian love that the author recommended (v. 22)? Can anything be done, on our part, to bring about this love, or does it all depend on God? Do we love people more as we get closer to them, or does "familiarity breed contempt"? How is our love related to our having been born again by the Word (v. 23)?

LESSON 20

1 Peter 2:1-25

CONTENT QUESTIONS

1. What sin did the writer want his readers to eliminate (v. 1)? ______
2. Why should they desire spiritual "milk" (v. 2)? ______
3. How should they feel about the Lord (v. 3)? ______
4. How had men treated the Lord (v. 4)? ______
5. If these people constituted a priesthood, what were they to do (v. 5)? ______
6. What was the promise to one who believed in the "chief cornerstone" (v. 6)? ______
7. What became of the stone the builders rejected (v. 7)? ______
8. What was the basic sin of those stumbling over this stone (v. 8)? ______
9. What titles did Peter apply to his readers (v. 9)? ______

10. List two differences between what they were and what they had been (v. 10). ______________________________

____

11. What specific command did Peter give them (v. 11)? ________

____

12. What was to be their behavior, as seen by their Gentile neighbors (v. 12)? ______________________________

13. What was to be their relation to their king or supreme ruler (v. 13)? ______________________________

14. What was to be their relation to subordinate rulers (vv. 13, 14)? ______________________________

15. What would be accomplished by their submission to God's will (v. 15)? ______________________________

____

16. If they were free as Christians, what were the limits on their freedom (v. 16)? ______________________________

____

17. How were they to feel about their brethren, their fellow Christians (v. 17)? ______________________________

____

18. How were servants to regard their masters (v. 18)? ________

____

19. Would proper attitudes save them from suffering (v. 19)? ____

____

20. They were commanded to accept patiently the troubles they brought on themselves. How were they to take the trouble they didn't deserve (v. 20)? ______________________________

____

21. Who was their example in suffering (v. 21)? ________________

22. Did this example deserve to suffer (v. 22)? ________________

23. How did He react to suffering (v. 23)? ________________

____

24. How was His suffering related to our sin (v. 24)? ________________

____

25. What influence did Peter see in this suffering upon himself and his readers (v. 25)? ________________

DISCUSSION QUESTIONS

1. How do you react to Peter's teaching about being submissive to employers, to rulers, to sufferings? Wouldn't his commands put an end to all progress? Should people in a democracy submit to rulers or organize to "turn the rascals out"? Should workers strike against employers? Should Christians be completely passive, doing nothing to improve their lot? Should people study medicine to eliminate suffering? How do we know when to submit and when to resist? What forms of resistance are permitted for the Christian?

2. What constitutes the reasonable or spiritual milk (v. 2) which leads to growth to salvation? To what extent must one put aside various sins (v. 1) in order to have the milk? Is it possible to partake of this milk by one's self, or must one drink in fellowship with others (v. 5)? If a new Christian asked you what he should do to achieve the best and most rapid spiritual growth, what would you advise? What would you warn him to avoid?

3. Why did Peter encourage his readers to grow toward salvation (v. 2) if they were already an elect race, a royal priesthood, and a holy nation (v. 9)? Had they already been saved? If so, in what sense could they still grow unto salvation? Should we speak of salvation today as something in the past or as something in the future? How do you prefer to think of salvation?

4. How can the "stone" be the chief cornerstone, elect and precious (v. 6) and at the same time be a stone of stumbling (v. 8)? Why should Jesus and His teaching be a source of offense to anyone? Is the teaching as offensive today as it was in the first

century? If not, is the difference because of changes in us or because the message has been robbed of its revolutionary nature?

5. How should a Christian act if he is to lead the Gentiles to glorify God (v. 12)? Did Peter contradict himself at this point, expecting Christians to follow Jesus, the stone of stumbling, while still earning praise from the Gentiles? How can one be offensive while still causing people to praise God? To what extent are modern Christians successful with these aims? Which is easier for us, to challenge and condemn the evil in the world or to encourage people to love and to praise their heavenly Father? What can we do to improve the manner in which we carry out these instructions?

6. Why is one required to suffer for doing well (v.20)? If God is a God of justice, why doesn't He see that good deeds are rewarded? If doing the right thing doesn't help us avoid suffering, what is the motive for doing right? Why should one try to live as a Christian, anyway? If it weren't for the hope of Heaven, or the fear of Hell in the next life, would you continue to be a follower of Christ?

7. In what respects do Christians constitute a "royal priesthood" (v. 9)? What constitutes the work of the priest (see Hebrews 5:1-3)? How do Christians, as a group, perform these functions?

LESSON 21

1 Peter 3:1-22

CONTENT QUESTIONS

1. What should be the relation between the wife and her husband (v.1)? ______
2. What should be the wife's purpose in acting like this (v. 1)? ______
3. What should be her behavior or manner of life (v. 2)? ______
4. What should she avoid when getting dressed up (v. 3)? ______
5. How should she dress herself (v. 4)? ______
6. What examples did Peter cite (v. 5)? ______
7. Give one such example (v. 6). ______
8. How should husbands treat their wives (v. 7)? ______
9. What should be the husband's purpose in acting like this (v. 7)? ______
10. What qualities of mind did Peter desire in all his readers (v. 8)? ______
11. How should they react when receiving ill-treatment (v. 9)? ______

12. If one wants a good life, what should he control (v. 10)? ___

____

13. What goal should one seek (v. 11)? ______________

____

14. How does the Lord react toward our behavior (v. 12)?______

____

15. Did Peter expect anyone to hurt those who tried to do good (v. 13)?______________________________

16. If one did suffer for righteousness sake, how should he react (v. 14)? ______________________________

17. What should the Christian always be ready to do (v. 15)? ___

____

18. If the Christian had a clear conscience, who would be put to shame (v. 16)? ______________________________

19. Why did Christ, the righteous one, have to suffer (v. 18)?

____

20. What other group heard Christ preaching in the spirit (vv. 19, 20)? ______________________________

21. How many of that group were saved (v. 20)? ______________

22. What is the saving power of baptism (v. 21)? ______________

____

23. Where is Jesus Christ (v. 22)? ______________________

24. What authority does He have (v. 22)?______________________

____

DISCUSSION QUESTIONS

1. What do you think of Peter's treatment of the marriage relationship? Was he being fair to women? Do you think he would give the same advice today? How would he feel about the various

aims of the modern movement to liberate women? Should the church today take a position on women's liberation? If so, what? How can Christian families help young girls to have the Christian point of view on this subject?

2. What do you think of Peter's advice to husbands (v. 7)? Would wives appreciate this type of husband? Would the move to liberate women be necessary if husbands followed Peter's instructions? To what extent do you feel that male obedience to these commands would bring an end to the struggle for women's liberation? How can Christian families help young boys to have the Christian point of view on this subject?

3. How would Peter feel about protesting social injustices, racial prejudices, economic problems, and the like? Would his advice about being a blessing and seeking peace be of any help in these areas? How can a Christian be "followers of that which is good" (v. 13) while at the same time seeking peace (v. 11)? How can one know when to seek peace and when to stand up for one's rights? Which is more important, to seek justice for the oppressed or to be able to give reasons for one's Christian hope (v. 15)? Compare Matthew 25:31-46.

4. If you were asked to give a reason for your Christian hope, what would you say? What is the basic hope of the Christian? Does it pertain to this life or the next? Why do you maintain this hope? On what evidence do you base it? (Cite example of evidence from the New Testament.)

5. In what sense did Christ preach to those who were disobedient in Noah's day (vv. 19, 20)? When did this preaching take place? Does this Scripture mean that people will have the chance to hear the gospel and repent even after death? If not, would it mean that Christ is always present whenever the gospel is proclaimed?

6. In what sense does the water of baptism become an instrument of salvation (v. 21)? Could one be saved by baptism, even though he has no faith or understanding? Should one be regarded as being "saved" before he is baptized? If one commits his life to Christ and then is suddenly killed before he can be baptized, would he be saved and go to Heaven? If so, in what way can baptism be said to "save" us? If not, is salvation by works rather than by faith?

LESSON 22

1 Peter 4:1-19

CONTENT QUESTIONS

1. In view of Christ's suffering, what did Peter want his readers to do (v.1)? ______
2. What should be their aim, while living in the flesh (v. 2)? ______
3. What had been some of their past sins (v. 3)? ______
4. Who continued to desire these things (v. 3)? ______
5. What did these Gentiles think about the changed lives of the Christians (v. 4)? ______
6. To whom will people give an account of what they have done (v. 5)? ______
7. Why was the gospel proclaimed (v. 6)? ______
8. What event was at hand (v. 7)? ______
9. Therefore, how should these Christians react (v. 7)? ______
10. In what respect were they to be especially fervent (v. 8)? ______

11. How were they to treat one another (v. 9)? ________________

____

12. How were they to use their special gifts (v. 10)? ____________

____

13. What was to be the objective of everything they did (v. 11)?

____

14. Why had some fiery trial come upon them (v. 12)? __________

____

15. What was to be their reaction to this trial (v. 13)? __________

____

16. Why should being reproached for Christ's name be a blessing (v. 14)? ____

17. What type of suffering should they avoid (v. 15)? __________

____

18. Of what type of suffering should they be proud (v. 16)? _____

____

19. Where was judgment beginning (v. 17)? ________________

____

20. If judgment began there, who should be especially fearful (vv. 17, 18)? ________________________________

21. What should one do in the midst of suffering (v. 19)? ______

____

DISCUSSION QUESTIONS

1. Should the Christian today expect to suffer for his faith, after the pattern of his Lord (v. 1)? What are some of the ways that Christians might suffer? Would a lack of suffering indicate something wrong with our faith? If suffering is bound to come to the Christian, how should we prepare young people for this experience? Is it honest to reach the unconverted by talking

about the joys of the Christian life? Would an honest appeal say something about suffering and sacrifice also? What is the basis of our message to the non-Christian?

2. What do you think of Peter's list of sins (v. 3) which distinguish the Christian from the Gentile? Would this same list apply today? What are the common and popular sins in America which the Christian avoids? Will the Christian life be as different and distinct in our culture as it was in the first century, or has our culture absorbed more Christian elements? Should the Christian today work to be "different," even though the differences do not involve actual sins?

3. What did Peter mean when he wrote of the gospel being preached to the "dead" (v. 6)? Does one who has never heard the gospel have a chance to hear it after he dies? Was Peter talking about people who were alive but spiritually dead? Or was he writing of people who heard the gospel preached while they were alive, but who had died before the time of this writing? In view of all that you know about the gospel, which of these views do you find more probable?

4. List the positive qualities which Peter recommended to his readers. Do you see any relationship between this list (vv. 7-11) and the list of Gentile sins (v. 3)? Which of these positive virtues would you consider most important in our day? Which do you think is most needed in your own church fellowship? Which would you regard as most needed in your own Christian life?

5. Why did Peter emphasize the importance of hospitality (v. 9)? Can you see reasons for hospitality in a day when Christians were distrusted and in which they held their meetings in private homes? How would you feel about having church groups meeting regularly in your home? Is hospitality as important for the Christian today as it was in ancient times?

6. What did Peter mean by his statement that judgment begins at the house of God (v. 17)? How do you explain this statement in the light of passages (like John 5:24) which seem to say the believer escapes judgment? If the Son sets us free (John 8:34-36), will we be free from judgment? If those of the household are the first to be judged, what is the benefit of belonging to the household? Is it possible to have greater freedom in any area of life without also having greater responsibility? Does greater re-

sponsibility require closer inspection and judgment? How can freedom be maintained in the face of such requirements?

7. What is the real purpose of suffering in the life of the Christian? Would you agree that suffering helps us understand God as the righteous judge (v. 17)? Does suffering help us understand God's power as the Creator (v. 19)? Is there a danger that suffering will cause us to think of God as unloving and unjust? If God were truly just and required you to suffer as much as you have inflicted suffering on others, how much would you suffer? When we blame God for our suffering, are we saying something about our pride? What can be done to get people to see that God is love and that He doesn't want suffering for His children?

LESSON 23

1 Peter 5:1-14

CONTENT QUESTIONS

1. What group was Peter particularly addressing (v. 1)? ______

____

2. How did he classify himself (v. 1)? ______

____

3. What command did he give this group (v. 2)? ______

____

4. Should money be the prime consideration in their work (v. 2)? ______

5. What should be the nature of their leadership (v. 3)? ______

____

6. When could they expect to receive a "crown of glory" (v. 4)?

____

7. How should younger men act (v. 5)? ______

____

8. How does God feel about humble people (v. 5)? ______

____

9. How did Peter want his readers to act (v. 6)? ______

____

10. What did he expect God to do in response (v. 6)? ______

____

11. Why should one feel free to put all his cares and anxieties

upon God (v. 7)? ______

12. What should be the Christian's attitude of mind (v. 8)? ______

______

13. According to Peter, what was the devil doing (v. 8)? ______

______

14. How did he want his readers to react to the devil's actions (v. 9)? ______

15. Were these Christians to regard themselves as alone in suffering (v. 9)? ______

16. What had God already done for them (v. 10)? ______

______

17. What should they expect God to do (v. 10)? ______

______

18. How did Peter feel about God (v. 11)? ______

______

19. What messenger had Peter used in this writing (v. 12)? ______

______

20. What was the real point of all he had said (v. 12)? ______

______

21. Who joined Peter in sending greetings (v. 13)? ______

______

22. How did Peter feel about Mark (v. 13)? ______

______

23. How were the Christians to salute or to greet one another (v. 14)? ______

DISCUSSION QUESTIONS

1. How should an elder or pastor "tend the flock" of the Christians he leads (v. 2)? What would his duties include? How much

power should he have over his flock? Should one look to his minister for an understanding of the Bible, or should one read it for himself? Is it proper and wise to pay a salary to church leaders, or should they be expected to earn a living at other work?

2. Is humility really a virtue (v. 5)? If all Christians were humble, how would we ever find those to assume positions of leadership? Is it possible for one to be too humble? Is it more difficult for a man to be humble than for a woman? Do modern churches help their members to be humble? As you think of all the positions of responsibility in the modern church—in teaching, witness, speaking, leading worship, singing—is there any work that promotes humility? What can the local church do to keep its active members humble?

3. How can a Christian recognize the devil, his adversary? Is this enemy easily recognized by the way he looks? In what forms does he come? Is he ever found in churches or in meetings of Christians? Should we think of him as personality or merely as an evil influence? How can he be defeated? What should churches be doing to prepare their members to meet such attacks on their faith?

4. What did Peter mean by commanding the younger to be subject to the elder (v. 5)? Was he talking about chronological age or about maturity in the faith? Should young people always be subject to their elders? How should Christian children handle this situation if they are reared in a non-Christian home? How can young people develop maturity if they must always be subject to elders? Should one respect his elders if they are doing wrong? (See Ephesians 6:1-4 for further insight.) To what extent do our current social problems stem from young people refusing to be subject to the older?

5. What do you think of the motives which Peter used in appealing to his listeners? Should one be humble in order that he may be exalted later (v. 6)? Should one be a good example in order to gain a crown of glory (v. 4)? Should one be humble in order to receive God's favor (v. 5)? Should one remain faithful in suffering to receive God's strength (v. 10)? What is the basic motive for living a Christian life? How should we utilize motives in teaching young people?

LESSON 24

2 Peter 1:1-21

CONTENT QUESTIONS

1. To whom was Peter writing (v. 1)? ____________________
2. What did he wish for them (v. 2)? ____________________

   ____
3. What had the divine power of the Lord already given them (v. 3)? ____________________
4. According to the divine promises, what would they receive (v. 4)? ____________________
5. According to these same promises, what would they escape (v. 4)? ____________________
6. Peter then listed the various qualities he wanted them to have. In addition to their basic faith, they were to add __________

   ____________________ (v. 5)
7. Next came ____________________ (v. 5)
8. Beyond this was ____________________ (v. 6)
9. Then ____________________ (v. 6)
10. And then ____________________ (v. 6)
11. Then ____________________ and

    ____________________ (v. 7)
12. If they had all these things, what would be the result (v. 8)? ____________________

13. What would be the result of lacking these things (v. 9)?

____

14. What would they avoid, if they did these things (v. 10)?

____

15. What would they receive (v. 11)? _______________

____

16. What was Peter always ready to do (v. 12)? _______________

____

17. How did he want to stir them up (v. 13)? _______________

____

18. What had the Lord Jesus made known to him (v. 14)? _______________

____

19. What did Peter want them to be able to do later on (v. 15)?

____

20. Why was Peter certain that his teachings about Jesus were not fables (v. 16)? _______________

21. What had the voice of God said about Jesus (v. 17)? _______________

____

22. When had Peter heard this saying (v. 18)? _______________

____

23. How long did Peter want his readers to heed his word of prophecy (v. 19)? _______________

24. What principle did Peter specify about the interpretation of prophecy (v. 20)? _______________

25. What is the source of prophecy (v. 21)? _______________

____

DISCUSSION QUESTIONS

1. What do you think of Peter's list of virtues given in this chapter (vv. 5-7)? Is the list complete? Are they in the right order? Does each one grow out of the previous one as they are listed? Where does the responsibility lie for adding each of these things, with us or with God? What can we do to help one another along this continuous process of growth?

2. Is it true that God's power furnished all of the necessities of life for the Christian (v. 3)? What would you include in your list of necessities? Would your children have a similar list? What makes something really necessary rather than merely desirable? Is our list of necessities different than that of our parents? What do you think would have been on Peter's list of necessities in view of his condition (see vv. 14, 15)? If God supplies the things which are truly necessary, how can we learn to be content with what He supplies?

3. What did Peter mean by asking his readers to make their calling and election sure (v. 10)? Can Christians be certain about their calling and election? If salvation depends upon God, what could Christians possibly do to insure their election? How would you explain these words in the light of such passages as Ephesians 2:8, 9? How much of our entrance into Christ's kingdom (v. 11) depends on us and how much upon God?

4. How important was it for Peter to enable his readers to remember certain things (v. 12)? What do Christians need to remember? Do people really like to remember familiar things, or do they prefer the new and strange (see 2 Timothy 4:3, 4)? Does your answer to this question help you understand certain modern cults and practices? What can be done to make remembering the familiar more attractive than the new and unusual?

5. What did Peter mean by telling his readers they would never fall (v. 10)? Is it possible for any human being to live as a Christian without stumbling? What should be done by other Christians when one of their number stumbles? How can we prevent the mistakes of one person from being followed by others? Was it easier to live a perfect life in Peter's day than it is today?

6. How do you understand the principle that no prophecy is of private or special interpretation? Does every Christian have the

right to read and interpret for himself? To what extent should we look to the clergy as guides in interpretation? To what extend does the Holy Spirit guide in the interpretation of the Word of God? If the Spirit guides each individual, would the effect be to add or to subtract material from the written Word (see Revelation 22:18, 19)? If the Spirit does not guide, would the effect be possible misunderstanding of the Word? Why do churches interpret the Bible in different ways? Why didn't the Spirit produce a book which cannot be misunderstood?

LESSON 25

2 Peter 2:1-22

CONTENT QUESTIONS

1. What did Peter anticipate that false teachers would do (v. 1)? ____________________

2. What judgment would they bring on themselves (v. 1)? ______

____

3. How successful would they be in gaining a hearing (v. 2)?

____

4. What did Peter see to be the motive of these teachers (v. 3)? ____________________

5. What did God do to angels who sinned (v. 4)? ____________

____

6. How many did God save out of a sinning world (v. 5)? ______

____

7. What did God do to Sodom and Gomorrha (v. 6)? ________

____

8. How did Lot feel about the evil life around him (v. 7)?______

____

9. What sort of person was Lot (v. 8)? ____________________

____

10. How does God differ in His treatment of the godly and the unrighteous (v. 9)? ____________________

____

11. What would you say about the courage of those unrighteous people who walk in fleshly lusts (v. 10)? ________________

____

12. Are angels as brave or foolhardy (v. 11)? ________________

____

13. What will finally happen to these foolish creatures (v. 12)?

____

14. At what time of day did these unrighteous ones conduct their revels (v. 13)? ________________________________

15. What could be said about their eyes (v. 14)? ________________

____

16. Whose example did they follow (v. 15)? ________________

17. What happened to this bad example (v. 16)? ________________

____

18. If these unrighteous people were like wells, what sort of wells would they be (v. 17)? ________________________

____

19. What did these people do to the better people around them (v. 18)? ____

20. What false promise did they make (v. 19)? ________________

____

21. What would happen if people who know the Savior became entangled in the world once again (v. 20)? ________________

____

22. Would they be as well off as those who never knew Christ at all (v. 21)? ____

23. What proverb described their condition (v. 22)? ____________

DISCUSSION QUESTIONS

1. Is the danger of false prophets limited to Peter's day, or do we face the same problems today? Whom would you consider the false prophets of modern times? What are the false teachings? How can we identify false prophets? What should the church be doing to protect itself against false doctrines?

2. What do you think of the ancient practice of designing creeds to protect the church against heresy? Would we be well-advised today to insist on some basic doctrines, such as were expressed in the Apostles' Creed?

   > "I believe in God the Father Almighty, Maker of heaven and earth; And in Jesus Christ, His only Son, our Lord; who was conceived by the Holy Ghost, born of the Virgin Mary, suffered under Pontius Pilate, was crucified, dead, and buried; He descended into hell; the third day He rose again from the dead; He ascended into heaven, and sitteth at the right hand of God the Father Almighty; from thence He shall come to judge the quick and the dead. I believe in the Holy Ghost, the Holy Church of Jesus Christ, the communion of saints, the forgiveness of sins, the resurrection of the body, and the life everlasting. Amen."

   What problems can you see in insisting on a creed like this? What advantages? Do you think this creed has helped to reduce heresy in the church?

3. What do you think of Peter's feelings about Lot (v. 7) (see Genesis, chapter 13 and 19)? Do you think Lot was really that shocked at the sins around him? If so, why didn't he move? Did perhaps his wife have anything to do with it? Why did he move into a wicked city? Should Christians today try to live separate lives, or should they associate with a sinful world? What can be done to help those who live surrounded by sin to maintain their Christian standards? What do you think of the answer of the early Puritans who came to the New World to set up their own society? If you had the opportunity of such a move with a company of Christians today, would you go?

4. What causes "the way of truth" or the Christian faith to be "evil spoken of" (v. 2)? Is it still true that false teachings and heresies have this result? Can you think of other problems which aren't really heresies? How can the church protect its reputation against such things?

5. How do you reconcile the judgment of angels (v. 4) with Jesus' teaching about God's support of those with faith in Christ (John 6:37-40)? Were the angels created by God? Did each angel begin as God's faithful messenger? Was it God's will that the angels should rebel? If God did not spare angels, should we expect God to spare Christians who become apostate? What did Jesus mean by His promise that God would preserve those who came to Him and would raise them at the last day?

6. Which do you feel is more needed today, the warning against apostasy (2 Peter 2) or the reassurance that God loves and saves (John 3)? If you were talking to members of your church, which would you emphasize? What should be stressed in talking to young people? Which in talking to the elderly? As you think of all denominations or nationalities, which viewpoint would you emphasize?

7. When Peter wrote of the apostate as being worse off than the unsaved (vv. 20, 21), was he teaching degrees of punishment in Hell? If so, do you think there will also be degrees of reward in Heaven? What form do you think these various punishments and rewards will take?

LESSON 26

2 Peter 3:1-18

CONTENT QUESTIONS

1. How many letters had Peter written (v. 1)? ____________
2. What had he tried to do in these letters (v. 1)? ____________

 ____
3. What did he want his readers to remember (v. 2)? ____________

 ____
4. Whom did he expect to come in the last days (v. 3)? ____________

 ____
5. What would these people say when they came (v. 4)? ____________

 ____

 ____
6. How had the ancient world been created (v. 5)? ____________

 ____
7. How did that world come to an end (v. 6)? ____________

 ____
8. How did Peter expect his world to end (v. 7)? ____________

 ____
9. How long is a day with the Lord (v. 8)? ____________

 ____
10. Why is the Lord so patient toward mankind (v. 9)? ____________

 ____

11. What will the coming of the day of the Lord be like (v. 10)?

____

12. What will happen on that day (v. 10)? ______________

____

____

13. What question did Peter raise with his readers, in view of all this (v. 11)? ______________

14. What should Christians be expecting and desiring (v. 12)?

____

15. What should Christians be looking for (v. 13)? ______________

____

16. What sort of life should they be living (v. 14)? ______________

____

17. Who had already written these people about some of these things (v. 15)? ______________

18. What had ignorant people done to these letters (v. 16)? ______

____

19. What could result from this treatment of the writings (v. 16)? ______________

20. What warning did Peter give his readers (v. 17)? ______________

____

21. What did he expect of them (v. 18)? ______________

____

DISCUSSION QUESTIONS

1. Compare verse 16 of this chapter with chapter 1:20, 21. Can you draw some conclusions about the study of Scripture from this comparison? What keeps a person from being ignorant? From being unstable or unstedfast? Why didn't Peter compose

his own commentary on the writings of Paul if they were so difficult? Is a position of church leadership any guarantee of learning and stability? If not, who should interpret Scripture for us?

2. How much attention should a modern Christian give to the words of the prophets and the apostles (v. 2)? Should a Christian know something about his own world as well? If he is to be a good citizen, does he need to keep up with government and world affairs? Should he be familiar with literature and the arts? What study habits should the Christian establish in order to keep a proper balance in all of these things? What is the function of the local church in assisting its membership in these things?

3. What is your understanding of the coming of the "day of the Lord" (v. 10)? What was Peter emphasizing here in his discussion of this event? Is the anticipation of this event more difficult today after two thousand years have gone by? Should we be better prepared today, when atomic power makes the dissolving of the elements a more likely possibility? Why is it that people don't take warning and prepare as they see history moving toward a climax in our time?

4. Is it true that "all things continue as they were from the beginning of the creation" (v. 4)? Can you think of changes in the world which have been brought about by Christ's coming? If not, how can we claim that Christ makes a difference? If Christ has brought about some changes, how could anyone say that things were basically the same? Why does evil continue to be so powerful in our world? Why do we still have war and hatred, religious persecution, economic and racial discrimination, and all of our social and political evils? Why does crime continue to increase? Why must we wait until God acts at the end of time to change these things?

5. Is the expectation of the "day of the Lord" (v. 10) a good motive for Christian behavior (v. 14)? Would the motive have been stronger if Peter had warned about individual death and judgment (see Hebrews 9:27)? Would a positive motive be better—to serve Christ because of His love for us (see 1 John 4:10, 11)? Is there a need for warnings to produce Christian behavior in our day? If so, what form should these warnings take? Should a warning about the "day of the Lord" be emphasized?

LESSON 27

1 John 1:1-10

CONTENT QUESTIONS

1. How far back in time did John start (v. 1)? ____________________

____

2. How much was he personally involved in these things (v. 1)?

____

3. Concerning what subject was he writing (v. 1)? ______________

4. What had John seen (v. 2)? ______________________________

5. What was the nature of life John had seen (v. 2)? __________

____

6. What was John's hope in declaring these things (v. 3)? ______

____

7. With whom did John have fellowship (v. 3)? ________________

____

8. Why had he written these things (v. 4)? ___________________

____

9. What was the basic message John was announcing (v. 5)? ___

____

10. How much darkness may be found in God (v. 5)? __________

____

11. Can one have fellowship with God and also walk in darkness (v. 6)? ______________________________________

12. How can we have true fellowship with one another (v. 7)? ___

____

13. What can cleanse us from sin (v. 7)? ___________________

____

14. How much of our sin can be removed (v. 7)? _____________

15. Can one honestly say he has no sin (v. 8)? ______________

16. What will God do for those who confess their sins (v. 9)? ___

____

17. What sort of cleansing does God offer (v. 9)? ____________

____

18. If one claims to be without sin, what is he saying about God (v. 10)? _______________________________________

19. What else can be said about the one who claims to be without sin (v. 10)? ____________________________________

DISCUSSION QUESTIONS

1. How would you reconcile John's promises with Peter's warnings? If the blood of Christ cleanses from all sin (v. 7), why should apostasy be any danger? Which do you prefer—the negative warnings of Peter or the joyous promises of John? Which do you believe to be most needed by Christians in our day?

2. What did John mean by the "fellowship" he wanted to have with his readers (v. 3)? Why did he have to declare certain things to them in order to have this fellowship? Why did the fellowship also include the Father and the Son? Is it possible to have fellowship or friendship with other people apart from Christians? Can one be a Christian without becoming involved in fellowship with other Christians? What is involved in genuine Christian fellowship? How involved should individuals be in the lives of one another? What can the local church do to promote such fellowship?

3. What did John have in mind when he urged the confession of sins (v. 9)? To whom should sins be confessed? To God? To some

minister or priest who represents God? To one another? To the one we have injured in commiting the sin? If we confess to God, is there a danger that we make forgiveness too cheap and easy? If we confess to human beings, do we often forget that all sin is against God and only He can forgive? If we require confession to all of these people, do we make forgiveness too difficult?

4. What should be the position of the local church in regard to the sin of its members? Should it emphasize the holy life in its teachings, or should it emphasize love and forgiveness? Should it have one teaching of forgiveness for non-Christians and another of holiness, justice, and punishment for its members? How should it go about identifying sin, making people conscious of sin, providing for confession of sins, disciplining those who do not repent (see 1 Corinthians 5:1-13)?

5. What is the difference in daily living between the Christian and the non-Christian? If Christians still have sin (v. 8) and still continue to do sin (v. 10), how are they different from others? Will the blood of Christ cleanse anyone from sin (v. 7)? What did John mean by "walk in the light" and by "fellowship one with another" (v. 7)? What should be the nature of the difference between the Christian and the non-Christian?

6. What would you say about John's message (v. 3)? Did he have the proper motive for writing or preaching? To what extent did he proclaim his own experience (v. 1), and to what extent did he include teachings which he had heard from others? What did John omit which he probably would have included in writing to non-Christian readers? How would you compare John's writing with the preaching to church members heard from most pulpits in modern times?

LESSON 28

1 John 2:1-29

CONTENT QUESTIONS

1. Why was John writing these things (v. 1)? ________________
   ____
2. When Jesus Christ took care of sins, how many people did He include (v. 2)? ____________________________
3. How can one be sure that he knows Jesus Christ (v. 3)? ____
   ____
4. What sort of people are those who claim to know Christ but refuse to keep His commandments (v. 4)? ________________
   ____
5. If one abides in Christ, how would he walk (v. 6)? __________
   ____
6. How long had his readers known the commands John was writing (v. 7)? ____________________________
7. Then on what basis might John be said to be writing a new commandment (v. 8)? ____________________________
8. If one hates his brother, what condition is he in (v. 9)?
   ____
9. If one loves his brother, where does he abide (v. 10)? ______
   ____
10. If one hates his brother, how good is his eyesight (v. 11)?
   ____

11. Why did John write to the little children (v. 12)? ______________

____

12. Why did he write to the young men (v. 13)? ______________

____

13. Why had he written to the fathers (v. 14)? ______________

____

14. How should one feel about the world (v. 15)? ______________

____

15. What things did John include as being in "the world" (v. 16)?

____

16. What happens to one who does God's will (v. 17)? ______________

____

17. Why did John think it was "the last time" (v. 18)? ______________

____

18. Why hadn't these antichrists continued in the fellowship (v. 19)?

____

19. How well informed were John's readers (v. 21)? ______________

____

20. What was characteristic of these antichrists (v. 22)? ______________

____

21. What would enable people to abide in the Father and the Son (v. 24)? ______________

22. What promise would they have (v. 25)? ______________

23. Did John's readers need anyone to teach them (v. 27)? ______________

____

24. How did John want them to feel at Christ's coming (v. 28)?

____

25. What can be said of those who do righteousness (v. 29)? ____

____

DISCUSSION QUESTIONS

1. Is love of the brethren (v. 10) the only commandment that the Christian needs to be concerned about? If one always acts in such a way as to express genuine love, will his acts always be right? Is "love" often used as an excuse for immoral behavior? How can one be sure that he is acting out of true love?

2. How can one love in response to a commandment (vv. 7, 8)? Can children be commanded to love each other any more than they can be commanded to love spinach? What sort of love did John have in mind? How is this love developed? Is it possible to love someone you don't really like? If an individual truly loves his brothers and sisters in Christ, how will he act? What would you expect to see as evidence of this love? Can people have genuine love without showing it in some way? Do we sometimes need help in learning to express our love? How can Christians help one another to love more deeply and to express that love more clearly?

3. What is involved in living a Christian life which is separated from "the world" (v. 15)? Does a Christian have to be involved with the world to some extent in order to live? How should Christians maintain their separation from the world in such areas as paying taxes, serving in the armed forces, holding political office, celebrating Christmas or Easter, sending children to public schools, and the like? Is separation from the world more difficult in our day than it was in John's? How can a Christian be separate from the world and still function as a missionary or evangelist to convert people in "the world"? Would complete separation make missionary work impossible?

4. What are the characteristics of the antichrist that John understood (vv. 19, 22)? Are there those in our day who would qualify?

5. How do you explain the apparent contradictiions in this chapter? If John's readers do not need teaching (v. 27), why does he write to keep them from sin (v. 1)? If his readers know all things (v.

20), how can he give them a commandment which will be new (v. 8)? If those who are genuine Christians will continue as genuine Christians (v. 19), why is John concerned that they might not abide (v. 24)? What do these differences indicate about the way John wrote and the way we should understand him?

LESSON 29

1 John 3:1-24

CONTENT QUESTIONS

1. Whose children did John consider his readers to be (v. 1)?
____
2. Why didn't the world recognize them as such (v. 1)? ________
____
3. What did John expect them to be like in the future (v. 2)? ____
____
4. What would this hope do for those who had it (v. 3)? _______
____
5. What is the nature of sin (v. 4)? __________________
6. Why was God made manifest to man (v. 5)? _____________
____
7. If one sins, does he know God (v. 6)? ________________
8. What might be said of one who acts righteously (v. 7)? ______
____
9. Why was the Son of God made manifest (v. 8)? ___________
____
10. Why would it be impossible for one who is begotten of God to sin (v. 9)? ______________________________
11. What were listed as characteristics of the devil's children (v. 10)? ______________________________

12. What was the message that all heard from the beginning (v. 11)? ______

13. Why did Cain kill his brother (v. 12)? ______

______

14. How did the world feel about Christians (v. 13)? ______

______

15. How can one know he has passed out of death and into life (v. 14)? ______

16. What makes one a murderer (v. 15)? ______

______

17. Since Christ laid down His life, what should His followers do (v. 16)? ______

18. What would be the evidence that one lacks the love of God (v. 17)? ______

19. How did John command his readers to love (v. 18)? ______

______

20. If we love in deed and in truth, what can we know for sure (v. 19)? ______

21. Who is greater than our heart (v. 20)? ______

22. If our hearts do not condemn us, how should we feel (v. 21)?

______

23. Then what may we expect to receive (v. 22)? ______

______

24. What is God's commandment (v. 23)? ______

______

25. How can we know God abides in us (v. 24)? ______

______

DISCUSSION QUESTIONS

1. How do you understand John's teaching about sin? If a Christian does not sin (v. 6), why does he need to confess his sins (1 John 1:9)? Do you think John could be talking about different kinds of sin? If the type of sin discussed in this chapter may be defined as "transgression" (v. 4), how would you define the sin discussed in the first chapter? If John was describing the ideal Christian life in this chapter, how close would modern Christians come to measuring up to this ideal? Do you think they have improved any over the Christians of John's day?

2. Which is more important in the Christian life, to avoid sin (v. 8) or to do righteousness (v. 7)? Is it possible to have one without the other? Where should we place the emphasis as we try to teach young people and to instruct new Christians of all ages? Do these matters require special instruction, or does one take care of such behavior problems automatically when the Holy Spirit comes into his life?

3. How does one develop Christian love? Does this love come by itself when we become Christians (v. 14), or do we develop it in obedience to a commandment (v. 23)? If God brings love into our hearts, why did John command his readers to love in truth (v. 18)? If love requires effort on our part, what should we do? How can we grow in love? What develops genuine love between husband and wife, between parents and children, between people of various races and economic levels (v. 17)? What can a church do to foster such love among its members?

4. Did John really expect God to give people whatever they asked of Him (v. 22)? Are there other requirements for having our prayers answered besides those which John mentioned? How do you think John would feel about those times when we ask for things we shouldn't have? Should we always pray for the recovery of those who are ill? If so, and if we received what we asked, would anyone ever die? Is this teaching about prayer dangerous in that it encourages us to ask for things and then causes us to lose faith when we don't get them?

5. How would you compare John's picture of God in this chapter with that of the Hebrews' writer (Hebrews 12:18-29)? Can you find elements of awe and respect for God in John's teaching, or did he focus entirely upon God as the loving Father? Which view

of God do you personally find most appealing? Which do you think is most needed among Christians today? Which view of God would be most effective in converting sinners—to warn them of a judgment to come or to offer them the hope and comfort found in a loving Father?

6. What do you think of John's list of commandments which Christians are to obey (v. 23)? Is such a list adequate? If one kept these two commandments, would he avoid all the sins that John was warning against (v. 8)? Is the command to love one another sufficient for Christians today, or should people also be warned about specific sins? Do you think that every act which expresses genuine Christian love is all right, or are certain things sinful, no matter how one feels about them? Is our feeling of love a sound guide to follow in determining right and wrong, or is it too subjective and apt to mislead us? What should be the basic guide in deciding what is sinful?

LESSON 30

1 John 4:1-21

CONTENT QUESTIONS

1. What should one seek to learn about the spirits (v. 1)? ______

 ____

2. Why should one investigate the spirits (v. 1)? ______________

 ____

3. How may God's Spirit be recognized (v. 2)? ______________

 ____

4. What is characteristic of the spirit of antichrist (v. 3)?

 ____

5. What enables God's people to be victorious and to overcome (v. 4)? ______________________________

6. Who listens to the people of the world (v. 5)? ____________

 ____

7. According to John, who would refuse to pay attention to him (v. 6)? ______________________________

8. If one loves, what is his relation to God (v. 7)? ___________

 ____

9. What is God's true nature (v. 8)? ______________________

 ____

10. How did God made His love clear to us (v. 9)? ___________

 ____

11. What was God's Son sent to do (v. 10)? ____________________

____

12. In view of God's love for us, what should we do (v. 11)? ____

____

13. Since we can't see God, how can we know He is with us (v. 12)? ____

14. How can we know God abides in us (v. 13)? _______________

____

15. According to John, why did the Father send the Son (v. 14)?

____

16. What happens to those who confess Jesus as the Son of God (v. 15)? ____

17. If God is love, what can be said of one who dwells in love (v. 16)? ____

18. How should those who love feel about judgment day (v. 17)?

____

19. If love is perfected, what will that do to our fears (v. 18)?

____

20. Why should we love God (v. 19)? _________________________

____

21. If one loves God, how will he feel about his brothers (v. 20)?

____

22. What is the commandment for those who love God (v. 21)? _

____

DISCUSSION QUESTIONS

1. What do you think of John's guide to identifying false prophets (vv. 1-3)? If you applied this standard to current religious teachings, which ones would be eliminated? Which would not be

eliminated? Why are there such varieties of teachings and doctrines, even among those groups and denominations which confess that Jesus Christ is God? How can we distinguish what is true and what is false among them? Do you think that God approves of these differences, of these varieties of opinion about himself? How should we treat those who also confess Jesus as the Christ, but who hold views different from ours?

2. If only those who already know God will hear us, and if those who are not of God won't listen (v. 6), what is the use of trying to witness or to do missionary work? How would you compare John's viewpoint here with the views of Paul in Romans 10:13-15? Should Christians today limit their missionary efforts to those who have never heard the gospel, or should we continue to preach to those who have heard the message already and rejected it? What might we do to make our witness more effective to those who are already familiar with the gospel? What can be done to get Christians more personally involved in witnessing? What forms might that witness take?

3. What is the relationship between love and fear (v. 18)? How would you understand this love of God in the light of such teachings as Romans 11:20, 21; Colossians 3:22; 1 Peter 2:17? If these other passages teach that God should be regarded with fear, what kind of fear would still leave room for love? What does John's contrast of fear and love say about the nature of love? Which teaching about our feelings toward God is most needed in the world today? Which is most needed among Christians?

4. What form should one's love take? If God's love for us led to action (v. 9), how should we express our love for Him? Is it enough to confess our love in words (v. 15)? Are we obligated to do more than this? What should we do to express our love for one another (vv. 20, 21)? Does this love require words or deeds? Is the average Christian better at showing his love or in talking about it? Would you rather have those who love you express it in words or in actions? What can be done to help people become better able to tell others of their love? What can be done to help those who always talk about love become more sincere in acting out their loving words?

LESSON 31

1 John 5:1-21

CONTENT QUESTIONS

1. Who could be said to be begotten of God (v. 1)? ____________

____

2. If one loved God, whom else would he love (v. 1)? ________

____

3. How would one know that he loved God's children (v. 2)? ____

____

4. How difficult are God's commandments (v. 3)? ____________

____

5. What has overcome the world (v. 4)? ______________________

____

6. Who has overcome the world (v. 5)? ______________________

____

7. Who came by water and by blood (v. 6)? ________________

8. Who bore witness of this (v. 6)? ______________________

9. Name the three that bear record in Heaven (v. 7). ____________

____

10. Name the three that bear witness in earth (v. 8).

____

11. Of what did God bear witness (v. 9)? ____________________

____

12. In what sense would one who disbelieves God make Him a liar (v. 10)? ____________________

13. What did God give us in His Son (v. 11)? ____________________

____

14. What could be said of one who has the Son (v. 12)? ____________________

____

15. What could be said of one who doesn't have the Son (v. 12)?

____

16. Why had John written these things (v. 13)? ____________________

____

17. When will the Son of God hear those who make requests (v. 14)? ____________________

18. If He hears them, what will they receive (v. 15)? ____________________

____

19. What should one do if he sees his brother sinning (v. 16)? ____________________

____

20. Under what circumstances should he not do this (v. 16)? ____________________

____

21. What might be said of one begotten of God (v. 18)? ____________________

____

22. How are the people of God distinct from the rest of the world (v. 19)? ____________________

23. Of what may the people of God be certain (v. 20)? ____________________

____

24. What final advice did John have to offer his readers (v. 21)?

____

DISCUSSION QUESTIONS

1. What is the relationship between faith in Christ and obedience to Christ? If our love of God is based on our obedience to Him (v. 3), why would John say that our faith overcomes the world (v. 4)? How is love related to obedience? If we keep the commandments because we love (v. 2), then why did John include love among the commandments we are to keep (1 John 4:21)? How would you describe what happens in a person's life as he grows in obedience, in faith, and in love? Which comes first? How does one lead to another? Is there a danger that too much emphasis on obedience will lead to a works-righteousness? (See Romans 10:17 as you answer these questions.)

2. What did John mean by the three witnesses (v. 8) the Spirit, the water, and the blood? In what sense did these three bear witness to Christ (see Matthew 3:13-17)? In what sense can you see these three bearing witness to the ordinary Christian? Is it necessary for the Christian to have these three in his own life (see Romans 8:9), or just to know about them in the life of Christ? How would each of these three be found in the life of the Christian (see 1 Corinthians 12:13, Galatians 5:22, 23)? Can the Christian use these same three witnesses in testifying to other people of his faith? If so, what should the Christian do, or how should he live in order to be an effective means of witness?

3. What do you think of the eternal life that John wrote about (vv. 11, 12)? What is its nature? When does it begin? How long does it last? How do you feel about death (see 1 Corinthians 15:26)? What is the relationship between the eternal life promised the Christian and the experience of physical death? Is the usual funeral service helpful as a reminder of eternal life? How would you design your own services?

4. How do you explain John's certainty that God hears our prayers and grants our petitions (vv. 14, 15)? Would God be good and wise if He granted us everything we asked? How should we go about praying according to God's will (v. 14)? How can we know God's will? Do you think John is recommending some method which will enable us to have all of our desires granted? Is it enough for us to say, "Thy will be done" or "in Jesus name" in our prayers? Why is it important for us to know that God hears us when we pray (v. 15)?

5. What did John mean by "a sin not unto death" (v. 16)? What sort of sin would this be? Doesn't all sin result in death (see Romans 6:23)? In what sense can the prayers of one person result in the life of someone else (see James 5:15)? If one sins, does he have to ask forgiveness for himself? How can anyone else ask forgiveness for him? What did John mean by a "sin unto death"? Was he implying that some sins cannot be forgiven (see Mark 3:29)? Was John thinking of physical life and death or of spiritual life and death? To what extent is prayer for forgiveness a mutual obligation of all Christians? When we ask others to pray for our sins, are we in danger of starting gossip?

6. Who is supposed to guard the Christian from the wicked one (v. 18; check several translations of this verse)? If Christ keeps us from evil, how do you explain John's command to guard ourselves from idols (v. 21)? Where does my responsibility for avoiding evil end and God's begin? What am I supposed to do, and what is God supposed to do? Do I have a responsibility toward my fellow Christians to keep them from the evil one? How might I fulfill this responsibility?

LESSON 32

2 John 1-13

CONTENT QUESTIONS

1. To whom was the author writing (v. 1)? ____________________

____

2. How did he feel about them (v. 1)? ____________________
3. Where did he believe the truth was to be found (v. 2)? ______

____

4. How long would the truth be there (v. 2)? ______________
5. What three qualities did the author ask to be with them (v. 3)? ______________ , ______________ , and __________
6. From whom would these qualities come (v. 3)? From ________ ______________________ and ______________________
7. Why was the author rejoicing (v. 4)?____________________

____

8. Whose commands were being obeyed (v. 4)? ____________
9. What request did the writer make (v. 5)?______________

____

10. How old was this commandment (v. 5)?______________

____

11. According to the author, what constitutes Christian love (v. 6)?______________________________________
12. How long before had the readers heard this instruction (v. 6)? ______________________________________

13. How could deceivers be identified (v. 7)? ________________

____

14. What title did the author give such deceivers (v. 7)?________

____

15. In what respect were the readers to look to themselves (v. 8)?

____

16. Which ones did not have God with them (v. 9)? ____________

____

17. Which ones had both the Father and the Son with them (v. 9)?

____

18. How should the readers receive one whose teaching disagreed with this (v. 10)? ____

19. Why shouldn't they greet such a one (v. 11)?_______________

____

20. How much did the author have to say (v. 12)? ____________

21. Why didn't he write it all (v. 12)? _______________________

____

22. How did he expect the people to feel when he came (v. 12)?

____

23. Who else sent greetings (v. 13)? _________________________

____

DISCUSSION QUESTIONS

1. Was this letter really to a woman and her family, or was it to a church and its members? What evidence can you find that the letter went to a whole church congregation? In what respects would a congregation be like a family? If he were writing to your congregation, would he think of it as a family? What would you like to see done to make your congregation more nearly resemble a loving family?

2. What do you think of the writer's emphasis on obedience in relation to love? Does genuine love always involve obedience? Must the wife who loves her husband always obey him? Why shouldn't the husband who loves his wife obey her? Does love always require some outward expression? How strong is the love which your local church has for Christ, as demonstrated in words? How well is this love demonstrated in obedience to Christ? How well is it demonstrated in deeds (see Matthew 25:31-46)?

3. What do you think of the author's feelings about the younger generation (v. 4)? Do we join him in rejoicing when young people follow the truth? Are we really trying to reach the children of non-church people for Christ, or are we content to teach our own families in Bible school and church youth groups? Is there a danger that non-Christian young people attending church a few times might become involved with our children and lead them away? If we don't want our children playing with every child in the neighborhood, why should we want them associating with everyone at church?

4. What do you think of writer's teaching about hospitality (vv. 10, 11)? Does his advice contradict that of the Hebrews writer (Hebrews 13:2) in regard to showing love to strangers? How can one know when to show love and when to shut the door? How can Christians help the poor and needy without also helping the lazy or the malicious who take advantage of the Christian's generosity? Is Christian hospitality needed in modern times when the state takes care of human needs so well? If a Christian shuts his door to false teachers, is he avoiding his responsibility to witness to them and to win them from the error of their ways?

5. How can the spirit of the antichrist be identified today (v. 7; see also 1 John 4:3)? Which of the beliefs about Jesus Christ must a Christian accept? Must one believe in the supernatural birth, miracles, death as a substitute for sinners, physical resurrection, bodily ascension, glorious return? Which of these would the antichrist reject? Are any of these doctrines really necessary; is it sufficient for one to commit himself to living by Jesus' teachings? Is it necessary for the church to have some official creed in order to identify false doctrines? What should one do if he finds false doctrines being offered in church meetings, perhaps even from the pulpit?

LESSON 33

3 John 1-14

CONTENT QUESTIONS

1. What did the author call himself (v. 1)? ____________________
2. To whom was he writing (v. 1)? ____________________
3. How did the author feel about his reader (v. 1)? ____________________

   ____
4. What was the author's prayer (v. 2)? ____________________

   ____
5. How was Gaius doing as a Christian (v. 2)? ____________________

   ____
6. How did the author know this (v. 3)? ____________________

   ____
7. How did the author feel about this information (v. 4)? ____________________

   ____
8. What gave the writer his greatest joy (v. 4)? ____________________

   ____
9. What people was Gaius supposed to help in carrying out his Christian work faithfully (v. 5)? ____________________
10. To whom did they bear witness of his love (v. 6)? ____________________

    ____
11. What was Gaius to do for them (v. 6)? ____________________

    ____

12. Why had these people left home in the first place (v. 7)? ____

____

13. What support did they have from the Gentiles (v. 7)? ____

____

14. How should Christians treat these visiting brethren (v. 8)?

____

15. What should be the motive for this treatment (v. 8)? ____

____

16. What sort of a fellow was Diotrephes (v. 9)? ____

____

17. How did he treat this writer (v. 9)? ____

____

18. What would the writer do, if he came (v. 10)? ____

____

19. How did Diotrephes use his ability to speak (v. 10)? ____

____

20. What type of behavior did the author recommend (v. 11)? ____

____

21. What sort of person is really godly (v. 11)? ____

____

22. What sort of person was Demetrius (v.12)? ____

____

23. What was the writer unwilling to do (v. 13)? ____

____

24. What did he shortly hope to do (v. 14)? ____

____

DISCUSSION QUESTIONS

1. What do you think of the prayer that Gaius may have health and prosperity (v. 2)? Should Christians be praying this way for one another? Does this prayer place the emphasis on physical matters instead of on spiritual matters? Since we all must die eventually, is a prayer for good health one which must eventually be refused?

2. What is the relationship between Christianity and prosperity? Should the Christian expect that following Christian principles will make him a success in business or in his work? Which principles will tend to make him successful? Which will not receive much credit in the business world? Will such practices as tithing one's income (see Malachi 3:8-11) assure business or financial success?

3. What do you think of the split in this church between Diotrephes and Demetrius? What sort of fellows do you think these were, on the basis of the statements made here? What can church people do to prevent divisions of this type?

4. What should be the position of the church in regard to missionaries? How can one be sure that the money is being spent efficiently? Should each Christian follow his own conscience in regard to missionary giving? Should the local church make some effort to coordinate its efforts and to require (v. 10) its members to support those causes it approves and to reject those it disapproves? Should church members be permitted to make their own decisions when matters of basic doctrine become involved?

5. What do you think of churches and missionaries taking money from "Gentiles" (v. 7)? What dangers do you see in accepting contributions from non-Christians? Should offering plates be passed to the entire congregation, or should the local church be supported by its members only? What about asking inactive members for pledges? Should Christian schools and colleges accept government money?

6. What do you suppose Diotrephes would say in his own defense in response to this letter? (See 1 Corinthians 5:13 for a possible argument.) How would one know who was right and which side to choose in a case like this? How can such problems be solved today?

LESSON 34

Jude 1-25

CONTENT QUESTIONS

1. What important connections did Jude have (v. 1)? ______

2. To whom was he writing (v. 1)? ______
3. What did he wish for them (v. 2)? ______

4. What exhortation did Jude feel compelled to give them (v. 3)? ______
5. What teaching of certain ungodly men was Jude concerned about (v. 4)? ______
6. What was the fate of some of those coming out of Egypt which Jude wants all to remember (v. 5)? ______

7. What had happened to certain angels (v. 6)? ______

8. What happened to the cities of Sodom and Gomorrha (v. 7)? ______

9. In what respect were the ungodly men similar to these terrible examples (v. 8)? ______

10. What did Michael say to the devil (v. 9)? ______

11. How reasonable did Jude consider the ungodly men to be (v. 10)? ______

12. Give three other examples of judgment which Jude used (v. 11). ______, ______ ______ and ______

13. If these ungodly men were trees in autumn, what would they be like (v. 12)? ______

14. If they were waves at sea, what would they be like (v. 13)? ______

15. What was Enoch's warning to people like them (vv. 14, 15)? ______

16. How did these ungodly men treat other people (v. 16)? ______

17. What did Jude want his readers to remember (v. 17)? ______

18. What had the apostles of the Lord predicted for the last time (v. 18)? ______

19. How much of God's Spirit would be found in the ungodly (v. 19)? ______

20. How did Jude instruct his readers to pray (v. 20)? ______

21. What were they to anticipate (v. 21)? ______

22. If they were to have mercy on the sinner, how should they regard his "garments"—his sins (v. 23)? ______

23. Who could keep them from stumbling (vv. 24, 25)? ________

____

24. To whom did Jude offer praise, giving glory and writing of majesty, dominion, and power (v. 25)? ________________

DISCUSSION QUESTIONS

1. How would you identify the ungodly men whom Jude had in mind in this letter (vv. 4, 8, 10, 16, 19)? What were they doing? What sort of people were they? Are individuals of this type found in churches today? How could they be identified in modern times? Who has the right to sit in judgment on church members, saying that this one or that one is ungodly? Is there a danger that we all condemn those who don't agree with us? How can we be sure that we are not the ungodly people Jude was warning against?

2. How does one contend for the faith or fight in defense of the faith (v. 3)? Against what or whom would one be fighting? What form would the fighting take? Why does the faith need any defense; isn't God willing to defend it? What form should the fight for the faith take in modern times? If contending for the faith is necessary, how should we prepare young people for this work? Does contending for the faith involve anyone else, or is it the defense of our faith within ourselves, against our own doubts?

3. What did Jude mean by saying that the faith had once for all been delivered to the saints (v. 3)? Is God's revelation a progressive act in which we understand God a little better each day and in which each generation knows Him better than the last? Does the New Testament reveal more about Him than the Old? If the faith had been delivered "once for all" at the time Jude wrote, would later books of the New Testament be useless? What do you think about modern prophets who claim later revelations from God (see Galatians 1:8, 9).

4. Jude, like a number of other New Testament writers, was concerned about enemies within the church fellowship itself. How do you suppose this problem arose in the first place? Why didn't God prevent it? What might the apostles or other Christian leaders have done to prevent it? Would a carefully prepared creed

or an examination for membership have helped the problem? Should Christians today be more careful and selective in admitting members to local churches? What requirements would you recommend—a longer period of acquaintance, some tests and examinations, a vote by a jury of examiners, a vote by the whole congregation, passing some required courses of study?

5. To what extend should Christians become involved in condemning evil wherever they find it? Should such condemnation be left to God (v. 9) (see also Romans 12:19-21)? Did Jude contradict himself when he criticized the ungodly for slander and criticism and then spent most of the letter in slandering and criticizing *them*? How should Christians act on matters like this today? Should the evil in the person, in the congregation, and in the community be pointed out and condemned? Or should Christians sit back and let God do it? What form, if any, should the condemnation take? Should Christians become involved in picketing and protesting demonstrations? If so, what types of evil are clear-cut enough for them to stage a protest?

6. What do you think of Jude's recommendations for keeping one's self built up in the faith (vv. 20-23)? According to Jude, what should we be doing in order to grow as Christians? What did he leave out which you feel should also be included? Which of these things have you found to be of greatest value in your own Christian life? Which have you found to be most difficult for you?